"There's no reason why any healthy person should lack sufficient energy to work successfully if certain principles are followed. The three most frequent reasons why people fail to utilize most efficiently their energy at work are:

　1. Chronic procrastination
　2. Poor use of time
　3. Failure to tailor their working style to their personality style."

Let this book provide for you a workable solution to each of those deterrents to efficiency. Increase your energy and vitality, and get more out of life!

The Energy and Vitality Book

W. PETER BLITCHINGTON

LIVING BOOKS

Tyndale House Publishers, Inc., Wheaton, Illinois

ACKNOWLEDGMENTS

My thanks fo the following publishers:

Atheneum Publishers, for permission to quote from
Human Aggression, by Anthony Storr.

Hopkins Syndicate, Inc., for permission to quote
from *How to Cash In on Your Worries*,
by Dr. George Crane.

McGraw-Hill Book Company, for permission to
quote from *Be Glad You're Neurotic!*
by Louis Bisch.

First printing, Living Books edition, August 1983
Library of Congress Catalog Card Number 80-52559
ISBN 0-8423-0704-4, Living Books edition
Copyright © 1981 by W. Peter Blitchington

CONTENTS

INTRODUCTION

We all know some people, though they tend to be a minority, who abound with energy. They plunge into new tasks and projects with enthusiasm, get by on a minimum of sleep, seem to be always moving, always active, yet they still have energy to burn.

I don't promise that after reading this book you will automatically become this type of person. Nor will I overwhelm you with a success story of how I magically transformed myself from a weak, listless person into a vibrant, energetic go-getter by simply drinking an "energy milkshake" or some such remedy. Personality rarely undergoes such magical transformations. Rather, it changes gradually, as a result of constant effort and attention to details.

According to the laws of health I live a pretty good life, and always have. I maintain an excellent diet, take vitamins, have an interesting job, exercise frequently, and am in good health. Yet I still have periods of listlessness, lack of motivation, and lowered energy output. This used to bother me. I wondered what I was doing wrong—what was keeping me from having the boundless energy I saw in other people. It took me several years to find out that energy output is strongly influenced by personality. People differ according to the type of energy they have and the manner in which they typically display energy. The person with constant boundless energy is not necessarily the best worker.

In order to be effective, energy levels should be controlled, focused, relaxed, and calm. The effectively energetic person is not the one who runs around pell-mell, in a state of perpetual excitement. Often energy can be seen only through the amount of work a person gets done. And the excitable, active person is not necessarily the best worker.

One of the best studies on the nature of energy was conducted by Dr. Hans Selye.[1] Actually, Dr. Selye investigated the influence of stress upon the body's ability to adapt. But his findings and conclusions have clear implications for our understanding of how energy is generated, and how it can be preserved and used.

According to Dr. Selye, each of us has a certain amount of vital energy. This energy should be used up at the rate set by nature, for once it's depleted it can't be replaced. Vital energy, according to him, is like a bank account from which you can make withdrawals, but you can't make any deposits. Once the energy is used up, there is none left. In one experiment, for example, flies that used up their energy the fastest died the soonest. Therefore one of the major tasks of this book is to show you how to preserve your supply of vital energy so that you'll have plenty available in later years.

But effective use of energy doesn't involve just staying alive—remaining vigorous and healthy as long as possible—although that's a big part of it. We want to know how to increase our energy output *now,* how to get more work done *now,* and how to be vigorous and healthy *now.*

In order to accomplish that goal, we need to understand several laws or principles of energy output. These principles cover such topics as the influence of personality style on energy level, the effects that emotion and stress have upon energy output, the sources of energy and how to tap into them, and the ways in which energy is generated and maintained. I will also cover some key techniques that should be helpful in learning to work effectively and conquer procrastination. Hopefully, after reading this book, you will not only use and understand your energy better, but you will also come to appreciate this wonderful gift of energy that God has abundantly given us.

1. Hans Selye, *The Stress of Life* (New York: McGraw-Hill, 1976).

CHAPTER ONE
ENERGY AND PERSONALITY STYLE

Each of us has an "energy style"—a characteristic way in which we discharge and use energy. No one style is necessarily better than another. Each has its own strengths and weaknesses.

I've had people say to me, "If only I could be like John (or Jane). He (she) always seems so energetic." There are many techniques we can use to increase our energy output and our ability to work. I'll cover several of them in this book. But to a large extent your energy level is determined by your personality style. Each of us has a personality style; this style was strongly influenced by heredity. Since each person's style has some strengths and weaknesses attached to it, the best plan to follow is to develop and appreciate those strengths and try to keep the weaknesses under control. Don't go around comparing yourself with others—they have their own set of energy strengths and weaknesses.

Your personality style strongly influences the type of work you're best suited for. In fact, the amount of work accomplished may be the best indicator of energy level and effectiveness. This means that the active person who moves around quickly and is always enthusiastically and impulsively plunging into a new task may not necessarily get the most work done, especially at sedentary tasks.

In this chapter, I'd like to describe two of the most basic personality styles. These are not the only personality types, but according to masses of research data, they are among the most important. They are certainly among the most important when we talk about energy styles. These two personality styles are introversion and extroversion.

Whether you're introverted or extroverted depends upon how certain parts of your brain are organized. You have a bundle of nerve fibers that run from the base of your spine into various parts of your brain. These nerve fibers are called the reticular activating system (RAS). The RAS performs some very important tasks without which you would die. One of its main functions is to keep you alert and attentive. Laboratory animals, such as cats, whose RAS has been purposefully destroyed will lie down and go to sleep. If a large enough portion of the RAS is damaged, the animals will sleep until they die.

So if your RAS partially ceased to function you would lose your sense of activation and alertness. As a result, you would probably be bored all the time. Nothing, no matter how stimulating, would interest you. New friends, recreation, work—all would seem dull and unstimulating. You probably wouldn't be able to learn very much because most books would seem unbearably boring. Only the most earthshaking events—disasters, for example—would be able to arouse your RAS. The good side to this is that you would be less sensitive to pain. You would not be easily intimidated by other people. Events and people that used to frighten you would have little influence since there would be fewer fear impulses reaching the higher portions of your brain. In short, you'd be bold, aggressive, and tough.

What would you be like if the RAS worked too well? An overdeveloped RAS would produce the opposite traits from those listed above. You would be extremely sensitive to noise, insults, pain, and practically every other type of stimulation. You would be painfully shy in the presence of strangers. You would most likely be a timid worrier. Everything that happened to you would be magnified several times by your RAS. As a result, you would probably try to avoid unfamiliar events or people. On the positive side, a densely branched RAS would give you several advantages. You would be intellectually perceptive and discriminating. Your alertness and easily activated intellect would give you a fine ability to concentrate for long periods of time on even the dullest material. As a result, you would make an excellent scholar, accountant, or creative artist.

THE RETICULAR ACTIVATING SYSTEM
MAKES US INTROVERTED OR EXTROVERTED

These descriptions of the underdeveloped and overdeveloped RAS are very similar to the usual descriptions of extroverts and introverts. In fact, whether you're an introvert or an extrovert depends largely upon your RAS. There are other contributions, to be sure. But people who inherit an "overdeveloped" RAS will be predisposed toward introversion. Those who inherit an "underdeveloped" RAS will more likely become extroverts.

Over the years many psychologists have recognized the importance of introversion and extroversion in trying to understand personality. In fact, as British psychologist Hans Eysenck demonstrated in his research,[1] introversion and extroversion are among the most important general contributors to our personality styles. This is not to say that they are the only factors which determine your personality type. We are all molded by many different influences. But the introversion-extroversion dimension is one of the most important, especially in determining your energy level.

MISCONCEPTIONS ABOUT
INTROVERTS AND EXTROVERTS

The introversion-extroversion dimension is one of the most misunderstood sources of personality. If we were to take a survey to see which personality type—introversion or extroversion—

is the more desirable, we would no doubt find that most people prefer extroversion. People are reluctant to admit that they are introverted, even when they score in the introverted range on personality tests. This is probably at least in part a result of our culture. Introversion is out; and it has been for some time. Extroversion is in—so much so that you find introverts trying to act like extroverts and making themselves frustrated and unhappy in the process. I served in the army with one young man—an introvert—who couldn't accept his personality style. He was always acting the part of the hail-fellow-well-met extrovert. He tried to be friends with everyone he met. But he did so in such a self-consciously inept manner that he ended up making a nuisance of himself. He couldn't relax and accept his introverted nature.

It's no wonder that this state of affairs exists. Not only does our culture uphold extroversion and repudiate introversion, but psychologists as well tend to follow that lead. One fairly well known behavioral scientist recently described with some glee the results of a battery of personality tests he took, especially the part that found him to be an extrovert. That is subtle. If you want the axe-handle approach, consider this description from a book on self-improvement:

The difference between these two types is in the degree of selfishness each has. If you are self-centered, selfish of your time, disliking others, unwilling to share your time or thoughts or possessions with them; in short, if you're plain

selfish, you are an introvert. . . . On the other
hand, if you like to have people around, like to
lend your lawnmower and books to a neighbor, if
you will drive across town to take a cold remedy
to a friend at the office; in other words, if you are
unselfish about things or yourself, you are an
extrovert. . . .

Most of us are extroverted part of the time,
introverted part of the time. . . . But the best
personalities are those who incline to extroversion
rather than introversion. The reason for this you
know by now. . . . The personalities that win are
those that attract others. Selfish persons do not
attract. Unselfish persons do.[2]

No wonder introversion is out.

The sort of description is far removed from
the true nature of introversion and extroversion,
however. As will be described below, each style is
associated with a particular level of energy
discharge. Introverts are the ones who most
often feel that they don't have enough energy, that
they are chronically tired and fatigued, and that
they don't get enough work done. For this reason
I will concentrate upon the energy problems of
introverts.

CHARACTERISTICS OF INTROVERTS AND EXTROVERTS

An entire book could be written about the
various characteristics of introverts and
extroverts, and several have. But I've tried to
restrict myself to those attributes that are relevant

to energy. These should be looked upon as characteristics which are more often found among either introverts or extroverts, not as absolute traits *always* associated with either one style or the other.

1. *Introverts are more sensitive than extroverts.* Sensitivity can be a plus or a minus depending upon how it's handled. Sensitive people are usually more discerning, perceptive, and creative than insensitive people. But they are also more timid and withdrawn.

Hypersensitivity in part results from the RAS. Introverts, who have an overdeveloped RAS, are more likely to magnify experiences than extroverts. Introverts multiply the intensity of all experiences and events. This is no doubt true of social events. But it's even the case with bodily sensations. In one study, for example, introverts and extroverts were blindfolded and then handed several objects to hold in their hands. Then the objects were taken away and each person was asked to estimate the sizes of the various objects. The introverts, it was discovered, consistently overestimated the sizes of the test objects. But the extroverts did the opposite: they underestimated the sizes. Other similar experiments have demonstrated that extroverts reduce the intensity of their experiences while introverts augment the same. For this reason psychologists frequently call extroverts "reducers" and introverts "augmenters."

Now, the tendency to magnify or reduce the intensity of experiences greatly affects our energy habits. People who always seem to have abundant energy are usually reducers. They are not daunted by things that frighten and inhibit more sensitive people. Rejection, criticism, pain, discomfort, and other energy-inhibitors don't intimidate extroverts as much as they do introverts.

The finely tuned nervous system of introverts often makes loud noises unbearable to them. They sometimes magnify the intensity of even very soft sounds. Thus many introverts will report that they can't concentrate while music is being played; it inhibits their energy flow. The German philosopher Arthur Schopenhauer must have been an introvert, for he complained about the distracting impact of light noise.

Other minor irritations will often inhibit an introvert's flow of energy. One introverted boy I knew couldn't concentrate on his schoolwork if his clothes were too tight. He described in detail to his mother the type of clothes he felt comfortable wearing; if she bought other clothes for him, he wouldn't wear them.

One experience that seems to inhibit the energy output of introverts more than extroverts is that of illness. One young man, an introvert, made the following observation about his extroverted father: "It always bothered me that my father could work circles around me. Even when he got sick, he still had the ability to put in a hard day's work. When I get sick it's all I can do to get out of bed, let alone do hard work." This young man punished himself because he thought his father was a "better man" — stronger-willed and a harder worker. But in actuality the main difference lay in the father's tendency to reduce the intensity of his experiences compared with the son's predisposition to magnify the intensity of his own experiences.

The father's insensitivity to pain made it easier to maintain his energy at a high level despite physical suffering. But it also made him less sensitive to the feelings of others, and crueler in his treatment of subordinates. The son's sensitivity caused physical discomfort to interfere with the flow of energy. But it also made him more creative and sensitive to the feelings of others than his father had been. So there are advantages and disadvantages to both these personality types.

But as far as energy output goes, the sensitivity of many introverts does work a hardship. In the face of criticism or rudeness some introverts will often tuck their feelings inside and experience a loss of energy and motivation. Others burn up energy by brooding over the old hurts and resentments. So one of the central tasks for the sensitive person is to keep his feelings from interfering with his energy output.

2. *Extroverts are stimulation-seekers; introverts are stimulation-avoiders.* Several years ago, right after the "space race" began between the United States and the Soviet Union, some psychologists began exploring the effects of "stimulus deprivation" upon human beings. They wanted to estimate how long astronauts would be able to exist in spaceships without any contact with other people. So they hired college students to

live in isolated compartments as long as they could. All volunteers were fed, and their basic needs were met. But they couldn't listen to music, read, watch TV, or talk to anyone else.

Immediately after the researchers advertised for subjects, quite a few college students stepped forth to volunteer. They all figured that it was an easy way to earn money. And they could use the time they spent in isolation to think about important things, such as their future plans. Since the experiment was conducted between semesters, all of the volunteers planned to spend at least several days in isolation (they were paid by the day).

Well, what happened was that most were unable to stay in isolation for more than a few hours, let alone days. The lack of stimulation quickly proved unbearable. But an interesting secondary finding was that extroverts were less able to tolerate sensory deprivation than introverts. On the average, introverts were able to stay in isolation for a much longer period of time.

Many subsequent studies have shown that extroverts prefer a much higher level of sensory stimulation than introverts. Practically any activity that we could call "stimulating"— whether positive or harmful—is practiced more by extroverts. Research has shown, for example, that extroverts smoke, drink, have illicit sexual relations, break the law, and engage in dangerous sports such as skydiving and boxing more often than introverts.

The cause of this difference, as usual, is the

RAS. As mentioned earlier, the RAS feeds into the cerebral cortex—the higher part of the brain (the part we think with). And it is the job of the RAS to alert or activate the cortex. Now, in the case of the extrovert the RAS is underdeveloped. This means that the cerebral cortex will be understimulated, since the RAS serves to activate or stimulate the rest of the brain. So in order to feel comfortable, the extrovert must raise the level of activation in his cerebral cortex. In order to do this he seeks a variety of stimulating experiences.

The introvert, on the other hand, feels pretty comfortable with his existing level of cortical arousal. He doesn't feel the need to experience stimulating events because he is sufficiently stimulated by everyday, ordinary events. Many people think that introverts don't like people because they avoid parties and don't enjoy meeting strangers. It's not that introverts dislike people. But other people are very cortically stimulating. Studies have shown that even looking into another person's eyes will activate the RAS and raise the level of arousal in the cerebral cortex. Being around strangers or groups of people is even more activating or stimulating.

Now one reason the extrovert enjoys going to parties and meeting new people isn't necessarily that he likes people more than the introvert, but rather because other people raise his degree of cortical arousal to a comfortable level. He is "turned on" when he gets around other people. When he's not around others, his level of cortical activation may be too low, and as a result he may be bored. But put him in a group and that's when he starts to click.

The introvert, as already mentioned, feels comfortable with his level of cortical arousal. When he gets around other people—say, at a party—his degree of activation increases to an uncomfortable level. Rather than being "turned on" and feeling good in a group of people, the introvert may actually feel the need to "shut down" his nervous system and flee from the situation that is making him feel uncomfortable.

This is one of the central causes of shyness among introverts: an overdeveloped RAS. One young woman I tested complained of extremely painful feelings of shyness whenever she met people outside the realm of her job. If you bumped into her at the grocery store, for example, and tried to start up a conversation, she would immediately get a frightened look in her eyes and begin looking around as if to find an escape route. She rarely looked you in the eye. And yet she was a beautiful woman, with little apparent reason to feel ashamed or self-conscious. But her test results showed that she was an extremely introverted person. Her level of cortical arousal was already so high that meeting an acquaintance pushed it up to an unbearable level.

What does this have to do with energy? Several things. In the first place, the need for extra stimulation makes extroverts more active and energetic than introverts. They don't necessarily have a larger supply of energy, but their energy more naturally spills over into action. That's why extroverts even move around more than introverts. Physical movement is a form of self-stimulation. Extroverts will even tend to choose jobs that require greater physical mobility, such as: parking lot attendant, salesman, public speaker—anything that requires moving from one place to another.

For this reason extroverts switch interests and activities frequently. One extremely extroverted friend of mine has attempted to earn extra money through a part-time job to supplement his income from teaching high school. But rather than concentrate upon one part-time job, he has had about five or six different supplementary jobs in the last two years. He's been a tennis instructor, a hang-gliding instructor, real estate salesman, and a stove salesman. The last I heard he had gotten into manufacturing.

Here is an important point to understand about introverts, extroverts, and energy: the fact that extroverts are more physically active doesn't necessarily mean that they are more productive. In fact, research findings indicate that introverts are more persistent than extroverts, and better able to stick to a task until it's completed. They may not appear as energetic, but they are more likely to get things done. Looks are often deceiving. Because a person is enthusiastic, active, and vigorous in his behavior doesn't necessarily mean that he is a productive worker.

But introverts do frequently have energy problems because of their stimulation-avoiding tendencies. It's easy for them to fall into a rut. They get into a dilemma: on the one hand they want to avoid stimulation and on the other hand everyone needs some stimulation to live. The introvert who always stays at home and never takes an active part in social activities may become bored with his life (boredom is a great energy-drainer) but afraid to do anything about it. He can form habits of lassitude and inactivity that may even come to influence his work.

3. *Introverts can concentrate more intensely than extroverts.* One of the great gifts of the introverted personality is the ability to maintain concentration for long periods of time. This gift of concentration gives introverts an edge in scholarship. They read more efficiently and make higher grades than extroverts. They are also more persistent than extroverts.

Apparently "mental fatigue" builds up more quickly in extroverts. Their attention lapses, they get bored, and they turn to something else for stimulation. This is probably the reason extroverts are more accident-prone than introverts. Studies have shown that extroverts have more traffic accidents and are given more traffic tickets than introverts; they also have more accidents on the job. Even extroverted airplane pilots have more accidents than introverted pilots.

But the shorter attention span of extroverts carries some advantages with it. Because extroverts are constantly shifting their attention, rather than focusing upon one object or thought, they are better able to "follow the ball" in social situations. Being a good conversationalist depends in part upon the ability to "shift set." Because the extrovert doesn't concentrate so intensely upon one subject, he is better prepared to hop from one topic of conversation to another. Introverts often prefer to talk about one topic at a time, in depth, without changing topics (thus exasperating more spontaneous persons).

As far as energy goes, this gift of deep concentration has both advantages and disadvantages. Introverts tend to have a "one-track mind." This tends to make them less susceptible to the sort of social distractions that tempt extroverts. The introverted student is not as likely to be lured away from his studies by parties, dates, and other social events as his extroverted peer. While they may not be as lively, active, and enthusiastic as extroverts, introverts are more likely to stick with a task until it's completed. They are thorough and meticulous in their working habits.

I've noticed these differences in introverted and extroverted writers. A book written by an extrovert will usually be marked by enthusiasm, confidence, and optimism. But it will also tend to be superficial and disorganized. A book written by an introverted author, on the other hand, is usually deeply thought out, thorough, and detailed. Sometimes it is so detailed that it becomes boring.

This gift of concentration gives the introvert a head start in scholarly or detailed jobs. But it can also cause some energy problems. Concentrating for long periods of time tends to wear a person out. Air traffic controllers, for example, have to concentrate intensely on their job of directing the flights of airplanes at large airports. Even a short lapse of attention could mean the deaths of hundreds of people. For this reason, the job of air traffic controller is a stressful, energy-depleting job. The average air traffic controller only lasts about five years on the job. Ulcers, emotional problems, and fatigue are common experiences. The long-term vigilance required on the job simply wears him out.

To a smaller degree introverts in their day-to-day living function like air traffic controllers. The hypervigilance and alertness of the introverted person may make him an accurate, conscientious, and persistent worker, but it also may wear him out and deplete his energy over the long run.

One gift that is found quite often among extroverts is the ability to take short, refreshing "cat naps." Bob Hope, the famous comedian, is known for his ability to refresh himself with cat naps. He can sleep in taxi cabs while on the way to airports, on airplanes, in between performances, etc. By taking frequent naps, he is able to get by on just a little sleep. He is known as a tireless performer, always busy, always on the go. These short naps are no doubt one reason for his boundless energy.

I've discovered that introverts are rarely able to take such cat naps. They find it too difficult to relinquish their intense concentration long enough to let go for a short nap. For this reason introverts are more likely than extroverts to be insomniacs. When the introvert lies down to go to sleep, his RAS is still actively feeding information into his cerebral cortex. Instead of drifting into unconsciousness, he thinks about the day's events and worries about the future. His body is ready for sleep but his mind continues to race.

The introvert needs to learn to punctuate his day with frequent rest periods, during which mental activity is suspended. It's probably expecting too much to ask that he learn to take short cat naps (although that would help his energy problems greatly), but he can at least put aside a few minutes each day during which he doesn't actively concentrate. This is especially necessary for homemakers. I've talked to many women who say they are worn out from having to watch their small children all day. They fear relaxing their attention because of the difficulties their children might get into.

One mother of a small child told me, "I feel like the weight of the world is on my shoulders. I can't relax one minute. I'm afraid that my little boy would get into something if I weren't watching him every minute. Or at least if I didn't know where he was. It's a great responsibility to have a child, especially if you're a Christian. Not only do you have to look out for his safety, you also have to be concerned about his character development and spiritual growth. With all this responsibility, I'm worn out at the end of every day."

I replied, "Well, doesn't he take naps during the day? Why don't you steal a few minutes of rest then? Why not take a nap when he does?"

"Well," she replied, "I could. But when he goes to sleep, that's the time I start thinking about all the things I have to do. I can get more done when he's asleep. I can iron, wash dishes, clean the house."

I asked her, "What's more important to you: to feel good and vibrant, and to age more slowly, or to always have a clean house, clean dishes, and clean clothes? Will it matter that much if you have to use paper plates a night or two a week? Does your house have to be spotless every single minute?

Fortunately, she saw the sacrifice she was making for the sake of appearances. I don't recommend irresponsible child rearing. It's a task that requires responsibility, attention, and self-control. But all three of these traits require energy to maintain them. The mother who is always tired will sooner or later have problems with self-control; and when her attention lags from fatigue, her sense of responsible care may also lag.

4. *Introverts are more inhibited than extroverts.* Introverts tend to be rule-oriented. They have stricter consciences than extroverts, and are more likely to feel guilty.

These attributes tend to make introverts more inhibited. They don't speak spontaneously; they rarely act on the spur-of-the-moment. Instead, they watch themselves carefully; they weigh each word before they speak; they ponder each impulse before they act.

While I was researching this book, I came across a young man who was inhibited and halting in his speech. Though intelligent and well educated, he had problems letting go. I asked for his opinion on a certain topic and he replied, "Well . . . I think . . . I guess I would say that . . . (long pause) . . . Yeah. . . . ." The entire conversation was like that. I knew that anybody who was that inhibited in speaking would likely have an energy problem. So I told him about the book I was writing, and he immediately showed interest in the topic. "Say . . . I could . . . really use a book . . . on energy. . . I don't feel like . . . I don't feel that I have very much."

It's likely that his energy problems were at least in part caused by his generally inhibited nature. Some introverts get so accustomed to always controlling themselves, always monitoring their self-expression, that they lose the ability to just let their energy flow outward, unimpeded. Their energy becomes dammed up inside.

Extroverts don't usually have this problem. They are less inhibited. On the contrary, they tend to be impulsive. Their emotions spill over easily into behavior. They move quickly and speak spontaneously. They bubble over with energy and liveliness, in contrast to the more sedate and controlled introverts.

But, as mentioned earlier, although extroverts appear more energetic, they don't necessarily get more work done. Introverts are more productive because of their persistence, concentration, and one-track minds. The extrovert is impulsive, and this may help him get started on a task. Instead of agonizing over whether to begin or not, he simply plunges right into it without thinking. But the problem is that, just as quickly, he jumps into another task without completing the first. This is one of the main problems with the impulsive working style of the extrovert: a half-dozen tasks that are only 75 percent completed.

It's true that many extroverts can get a lot done by hopping from one task to the next to the next and then eventually back to the first. But I find that a lot of extroverts who seem so energetic and confident are unproductive because they leave a string of unfinished tasks behind them. This is one reason why extroverts are so unorganized: organization usually requires concentration on one task until it's finished.

When I first began teaching at the college level I struck up a friendship with an extremely extroverted professor who was my age. He seemed to be always brimming over with energy. He was always busy at some task, always on the go, enthusiastic, confident, and active. At first I thought he must be the most productive member on the staff. And he did have a lot of things going. But a closer look revealed a string of uncompleted tasks. He would enthusiastically begin one project, and just as enthusiastically drop it in favor of another. Actually, many of his more sedate, introverted colleagues were much more productive than he.

5. *Extroverts are more optimistic than introverts.* Optimism is one of the main reasons why some people are more energetic than others. The optimistic person plunges confidently into new projects because he anticipates success. He looks forward to them.

But the pessimistic person fears exercising his powers in new projects. He too often expects failure rather than success. He inhibits his own flow of energy before ever beginning a new project.

According to research studies, a sense of optimism is found more often among extroverts than introverts. Sometimes a pessimistic attitude can be a beneficial attribute, if it's not overdone. The pessimistic person may be motivated to plan better and work harder in order to insure success. Mild pessimism may impel a person to put forth great efforts—he knows that success will come to him only after maximum efforts.

But more often than not, an optimistic attitude serves to increase rather than decrease energy output. The optimist is more willing to attempt new tasks—ones he's never tried before—than is the pessimist. His expectation of success is high, so his energy output is also high.

One of the best examples I've come across of the benefits of an optimistic attitude (from the standpoint of energy release) is seen in a book on marriage and child rearing that I read recently. In it the author describes the experiences that led her to give up a career orientation and become a full-time wife and mother. She begins by stating that of all the men she's known she can count on one hand the ones who were smarter than she is (this kind of blatant braggadocio comes almost exclusively from extremely optimistic extroverts); her husband was one of those men.

She relates that after marriage she and her husband agreed that she should seek any career that appealed to her. So she became a hospital dietician, taught an encounter group, formed her own tour corporation, worked in a construction company, taught school, attended agricultural college, and applied to law school. She further describes the many tasks that she quickly learned. She was the automobile repairman of the family, a skill she learned (when she was younger) from watching her boyfriend work on lawnmower motors. She also showed an admirable willingness to tackle new tasks, like breaking down the chimney in her home and rebuilding it.

In general, that part of her book is an excellent description of the power of optimism. This optimistic, extroverted woman eagerly plunged into any new task, no matter how difficult. She plunged from one task to another, learning all with ease. That's the advantage of optimism: those who have it don't fret over the question of how difficult the task is or how much work it involves; they just jump right into it. Their boundless energy and enthusiasm are amazing.

However, there is a drawback to this personality style—one that the author doesn't see. The same optimistic impulsivity that causes extroverts to plunge right into one task after another also makes them less likely to really develop a deep level of knowledge or skill at any one task. Any person who becomes a law student, an agriculture student, a teacher, a dietician, mechanic, construction worker, and so on will not be profoundly skilled at any of these. She will be a dilettante, learning a variety of skills but being master of none. So cheer up, introverts, and don't put yourself down because you lack the bounce and eagerness of many of your extroverted friends. Your specialty is depth, not breadth. And in order to achieve depth in any area you have to be willing to put up with boredom. Lack of that ability causes many extroverts to fail to acquire profound mastery or display true creativity.

6. *Introverts have more creative energy than extroverts.* If I were asked to identify the single most important advantage (from the standpoint of energy) that introverts have over extroverts, I would say: creativity. Introverts have a lot of creative energy. And unless they find a way to unlock and utilize that creative energy, the chances are good that they will feel frustrated and have energy problems.

This need of introverts for creative outlets shows up clearly in research on motivation. Psychologist Zygmunt Piotrowski, for example, tested and studied the behavior of many businessmen and high ranking executives.[3] He concluded that the more extroverted the person, "the more is a job or an occupation treated as a means for social advancement and the more are the individual's goals determined by the praise and criticism of others, especially his superiors on the job." On the other hand, the more introverted the person, "the more is the job treated as a means of personal improvement and the more are the goals determined by artistic, scientific, and other objective creative possibilities of the job."

In a book entitled *Be Glad You're Neurotic!*

Louis Bisch makes the same observation: "Introverts, to be sure, are the creative artists of pen, brush or clay, the inventors, the philosophers, the research workers, the people who fashion the new and startling. We owe almost everything that is cultural and genuinely civilized to the introverts.[4]

Finally, Drs. Edward Strecker and Kenneth Appel, in *Discovering Ourselves,* verify the above observations and add to them a description of both the strengths and weaknesses of the introverted and extroverted personality styles:

The extroverts get things done; they are the executives, the men of the world, the sociable, and cheerful people. The introverts are those who supply innovations and plan for the future. The present belongs to the one, the future to the other. From the lack of sociability, and from their detachment, introverts see more clearly problems and solutions which never occur to the extroverts. The introverts are dreamers and inventors. Many of the greatest discoveries have been made by them. Both types developed to the extreme are equally useless and harmful; the extrovert in senseless overactivity, and the introvert in aimless fantasy.[5]

Here are two of the greatest dangers that introverts and extroverts face in making use of their energies: extroverts may become caught up in a maze of purposeless, undisciplined, spontaneous activity, and introverts may fail to act upon their fantasies and dreams.

For the introvert, energy needs to find its way into creative expression. The introvert needs a creative outlet as much as the extrovert needs extensive social relationships. This outlet can take a variety of forms. An introverted dentist I know finds his creative outlet in gardening. A housewife makes stuffed animals for the children's class at her church. A technician hand-carves replicas of eighteenth-century muskets. The possibilities are practically infinite. Not everyone has to become a poet or an inventor to be creative. There are a variety of creative outlets available to anyone willing to search around. And I think that a creative outlet is almost indispensable for the introvert who wishes to make better use of his energies.

For the extrovert, energy output needs to be subordinated to an overriding purpose. The extrovert needs to put into practice that which comes naturally to the introvert: persistence at a single project until it's completed. This doesn't mean that extroverts shouldn't jump from one task to the next. But they should constantly remind themselves to come back to the first task until it's finished. Otherwise they will be like the man who got on his horse and rode off in all directions. Another habit that extroverts should borrow from introverts is that of disciplined thinking and long-range planning. Many extroverts fail to put their energy to the best use because of hasty, impulsive, poorly thought-out actions. They need to learn to devise long-range plans and goals and stick to those plans and goals until they've been completed.

SUMMARY:
INTROVERTS, EXTROVERTS, AND ENERGY USAGE

To sum up, we can say the following about introverts, extroverts, and energy. Introverts need to:

1. *Avoid overstimulation.* If your job is too noisy, or if it creates more stimulation or pressure than you feel comfortable with, you might consider another job. If big-city life is too noisy and stimulating, you could consider a quieter, more peaceful existence in a small town.

2. *Choose a creative occupation or hobby.* If you are an introvert who has trouble with energy, you might need a creative outlet. The introvert's drive for creative expression is strong. But it can be satisfied in a variety of different ways: writing, gardening, carving, and cooking are just a few.

3. *Punctuate your day with short rest periods.* Realize that intense concentration over time wears you out. If you are an introvert, you have the gift of deep concentration. But that gift can be turned into a liability unless you learn to snatch short breaks and rest stops. During these times you need to suspend concentration and allow your mind to drift. In the long run you'll get more done with these rests than you would without them.

4. *Don't be dominated by pessimism.* Continue to form thorough plans before you undertake a new project. But after the last doubt has been dealt with, let go of any pessimistic feelings you might still have. "I can do all things through Christ which strengtheneth me" (Phil. 4:13).

Remember that in order for energy to flow forth when you need it, you must have a feeling of optimism and confidence about your projects.

For the extrovert, most of this advice is unnecessary. If you are an extrovert, then the chances are good that generating energy is not a problem for you. The optimism and confidence of the extrovert just naturally increases energy output. Your major problem is concentrated energy usage. So the most important advice for the extrovert is: *Practice persistence and long-range planning.* Don't shoot from the hip. Use your energy in a concentrated, guided manner. And keep returning to your projects until they're completed.

NOTES

1. Hans Eysenck, *The Biological Basis of Personality* (Springfield, IL: Charles C. Thomas, 1977).
2. Charles B. Roth, *The Key to Your Personality* (New York: Permabooks, 1949).
3. Zygmunt Piotrowski, *The Perceptanalytic Executive Scale* (New York: Grune & Stratton, 1963).
4. Louis Bisch, *Be Glad You're Neurotic!* (New York: McGraw-Hill, 1946).
5. Edward Strecker and Kenneth Appel, *Discovering Ourselves* (New York: Macmillan, 1958).

CHAPTER TWO
ENERGY AND WORK:
HOW TO GET THINGS DONE

Energy is so closely associated with the ability to work that some people actually attempt to measure a person's energy level by looking at how much work he does. One writer observes that, "No other single factor plays so large a part in success as abundant energy. . . ."[1]

When a person indicates that he doesn't have enough energy, he's usually thinking about work. Most of us have few difficulties finding the energy to do what we really want to do. We rarely complain that we're too weak to work on a beloved hobby or engage in some type of recreation we really enjoy (though many of us could complain that we lack enough time to do these things). But all too often our feelings of tiredness, lack of motivation, listlessness, and lassitude center around our work, or at least around certain parts of it.

There's no reason why any healthy person

should lack sufficient energy to work successfully if certain principles are followed. The three most frequent reasons why people fail to utilize most efficiently their energy at work are: (1) chronic procrastination, (2) poor use of time, and (3) a failure to tailor their working style to their personality style (and, similarly, a failure to find the type of work that's compatible with their personality style). Each of these will be taken up in the following sections.

CONQUER CHRONIC PROCRASTINATION

I use the term "chronic procrastination" rather than simply "procrastination" for a reason. All of us procrastinate sometimes. Every single person that I've talked to about it says that he procrastinates at certain times. Many say they procrastinate at anything they attempt to do. So conquering procrastination completely would seem to be an impossible task. It's too deeply embedded in human nature. As William James, the father of American psychology, put it: "In the dim background of our mind we know what we ought to be doing, but somehow we cannot start. Every moment we expect the spell to break, but it continues, pulse after pulse, and we float with it."[2]

Sound familiar?

There's no pill we can take that will conquer procrastination for us once and for all. But there are some actions we can pursue and some tools we can use to keep chronic procrastination from inhibiting our flow of energy.

Chronic and persistent procrastination suggests a problem with your thinking—a self-defeating way of conceptualizing the task before you. You're guilty of thinking too big. This sounds odd, I know. Most of the books you see on how to adjust your thinking go by some titles such as *Think Big!* They rightly imply that everyone should construct high and lofty goals. No one should aim low.

But the kind of thinking I mean is the thinking you engage in right before you start to work, not the sort of thinking you use when you construct goals for yourself. When you see a task as *very large,* you feel small and inadequate in comparison. Thinking in terms of large tasks automatically inhibits your flow of energy. You've bitten off too large a mental image. Your energy level can't rise to handle it. You feel pessimistic and listless in the face of it. Through this feeling of listlessness your unconscious mind is trying to tell you something. Your thinking is inhibiting the flow of energy before you even begin. You put off this enormous task. You procrastinate.

In order to get your energy flowing outward into productive work, you need to reverse your mental processes. You need to *think small.*

When you get ready to work on a dreaded project, don't plan to do more than the very smallest amount of work. In other words, prepare to finish only the smallest possible unit. If, after completing the smallest unit of work, you decide to do more, that's good. If not, that's OK too. The important thing is to avoid thinking beyond the smallest possible unit of work. When you think small like that, a surge of energy and enthusiasm is automatically implemented. But when you think big, energy and enthusiasm are automatically dampened. Let me explain further what I mean with an anecdote.

When I first began writing I had a terrible struggle with procrastination. Writing is probably the easiest task to procrastinate about, anyway. Practically all writers report vicious battles with procrastination. Victor Hugo, for example, had procrastinated for so long before writing *The Hunchback of Notre Dame* that out of desperation he commanded his servant to take away his clothes and lock all the doors to his bedroom. The deadline for publication of the book was rapidly approaching and Hugo felt the need for drastic measures. So he had his servant lock him in the bedroom with nothing but pen and paper (and an occasional meal slipped over the door). With nothing else to do, he wrote. So well did this method work for him that he used it in all his subsequent writing endeavors.

My own struggles with procrastination had become so fierce that I might have considered Victor Hugo's method if I had known about it at the time. I tried to conquer the task at first by dictating hastily into a recorder and having my wife type it. This produced written work (of a sort) but a rather ineffective writing style.

To make a long story short, I tried first one method and then another, unsuccessfully, until I hit upon a solution. One day I began analyzing what happened when I actually got ready to write. Up to then everything seemed OK. I had done thorough research. I had a good topic. I was well prepared. So what was the problem?

The problem, I decided, was in my thinking. When I got ready to actually sit down and write, the thought of creating an entire book—a 40,000-to 70,000-word manuscript—completely intimidated me. I felt small in the face of it. It seemed that I would run out of creative energy long before I ever completed the manuscript. So I decided to stop thinking in terms of writing a whole book. I began lowering my sights. First I would think in terms of writing only one chapter; but even that was risky because I wasn't sure I could finish a chapter in one hard day's work. So I thought in terms of a page. Then a paragraph. Neither seemed to work very well. So I decided to think only in terms of a sentence. After all, even if you intend to write an entire book, you can do it one sentence at a time. (Actually, you can only do it one word at a time. But that was too great a reduction for my purposes.)

So when I get ready to begin writing a manuscript, I think in terms of one sentence. I know that I can successfully write one sentence. It might take me ten minutes, but I will do it. And my energy and motivation won't flag a bit at the thought of it. On the contrary, I can tackle one sentence with gusto, since I'm confident of success. So my daily writing quota is one measly sentence.

You're probably wondering: Won't I be terribly

unproductive if I think so small? All I can say is that my output has greatly increased since I've begun using this method. In the last two years I've written three books, one booklet, and several articles. This output was achieved despite a full-time job as a college professor.

By thinking small I've avoided the energy-depleting struggle over procrastination. Much energy is lost when you struggle with yourself over some task that you know you should be doing but just can't because it seems so big. And the longer you put it off the bigger it gets. I no longer have this struggle. I no longer punish myself for laziness and unproductivity (another energy loss) because I don't have to do any more than the bare minimum. My daily quota is one sentence per day. Any time I get ready to write I think in terms of just that one sentence. Any time the thought arises, "You have an entire book (or chapter or page) to write," I immediately push it out of my mind.

Now if you held me down and injected sodium Pentothal, or some other truth serum, into me, I might confess that underneath the surface I really expected to write much more than one sentence at a sitting. But I don't let myself think about it consciously. (You get the point?) And I also must confess that once I really get into a book, I find I need this method far less than when I first began. I rely on this one-small-unit method mainly at the beginning of a book, when I need help getting started, and at the very end, when I've just about run out of ideas and am sick of the entire process. During the middle part of it I seem to get a momentum established that carries me through most of the writing. But the point is that I don't have to tackle an entire book at one sitting. Some days I might end up writing twenty pages and other days only one sentence. Either is acceptable.

Try this method yourself if you have a chronic problem with procrastination. Think in terms of washing one dish or laying one brick instead of cleaning the kitchen or building a house. If you are a student, and you have trouble forcing yourself to study, think in terms of reading one paragraph only. You are probably thinking, "I have deadlines in the form of tests." But if you start early enough, the deadlines won't be such a problem. It's when you put them off until the last minute that deadlines start to frighten you. But if you think in terms of small units you will have much less difficulty getting started.

After all, isn't this the way you work? You can't read more than a few words at a time; you can't wash more than one dish at a time; you can't lay more than one brick at a time. So why should you think in terms larger than the one thing at a time you can do? All it will do is make you feel overloaded and inadequate to complete the task. And that feeling is the main cause of chronic procrastination.

Some psychologists might say that the real cause of your chronic procrastination is a poor self-concept. The reason you don't consider yourself adequate in the face of large-scale tasks is that you feel small. So the best way to handle procrastination is to improve your self-concept (by paying $35.00 to $50.00 an hour to a psychologist). In answer to that, let me say first of all that I haven't been greatly impressed with the ability of psychotherapy to strongly influence the self-concept. In the long run, if a person expects to improve his self-concept he will have to do the major share of the work himself. (If that's so, what does he need a psychologist for?) And one of the best ways to improve the self-concept is by acquiring the image of yourself as a competent, effective person. So if chronic procrastination is caused by a low self-concept (which I doubt), then one of the best ways to improve the self-concept is by conquering chronic procrastination.

In actuality, I think chronic procrastination is caused by mentally biting off more than you feel you can chew. Some people need to reduce a task to its smallest possible units, and then work on it, one unit at a time, in order to be enthusiastic about their work. I confess that I'm one of those people. I think that chronic procrastination is a sign that your unconscious mind is trying to tell you something: "Whoah! Put on the brakes! Danger ahead! You might not be able to do this!" Your energy system obeys your unconscious mind by shutting off the flow of energy. The way to avoid this is to think small. The more difficult the task, the smaller you should think. If you do that, you'll always have enough energy and motivation to complete any task.

THE ISSUE OF QUOTAS

Many writers, students, and businessmen set quotas for themselves. The quotas serve as goals, telling them how much is expected. When they've met the quota, they can stop. This is one way of handling the procrastination problem. But I have not found it as useful as the smallest-possible-unit method (at least in the early stages of a project) unless very small quotas are used. It's much better to set ridiculously small quotas and successfully meet them than to set large, ambitious quotas and consistently fall short. When this latter happens there is usually a loss in interest, self-esteem, and motivation. Once you've set a standard for yourself, your conscience will judge you according to that standard. It will punish you for falling short. So you can insure a loss of energy and a feeling of failure and defeat, before you ever begin, by setting large quotas—or a feeling of accomplishment, an increase in self-esteem, and a rise in energy level by setting small quotas.

I've seen many people fail miserably because they started out on a project with too high an expectation of what they could do. This has been especially true with new exercise programs. A young man I knew decided that he'd like to build his body up, so he bought several books on weight training. As he looked through the books he found first one exercise and then another that he thought he should have in his weight training program. I tried to get him to start off with just one or two exercises, at least until he had established a habit of exercising, but his enthusiasm and confidence knew no bounds. He ended up with no fewer than twelve different exercises, and a two-hour exercise routine. He lasted about two months. To my knowledge he's never picked up a weight since then. About two hundred dollars worth of exercise equipment gathers dust in his basement. It's much better to plan on doing one exercise and stick with it than to devise an olympic training routine and fall short of the mark.

To me, even setting time quotas is risky. Some experts advise people to set aside small quotas of time, say five minutes, and work at the task for only that long. Then when you've become accustomed to five minutes, raise the quota to ten, then fifteen, etc. I find that this doesn't work so well for me for at least two reasons.

In the first place, perhaps because my major procrastination task is writing, I'm more interested in quality. To say, "I'll work on something for five minutes," doesn't say anything about either quality or quantity. I could work for five minutes and have only half a sentence written (or none at all). It could be either poor or good quality. But when I think in terms of one sentence, I'm much better able to concentrate on quality. I'm thinking about the task rather than the time.

In the second place, by always thinking in terms of the smallest possible unit (one sentence) as my quota, and never raising that to a page or a paragraph, I insure a continuous experience of success. We all have days when our energy level is low, our motivation sags, or other more pressing demands arise. If you raise your quota frequently, you will inevitably be faced with a high quota on one of these low days. It's better, in that case, to set low standards.

The idea behind the raising of quotas is sound. You want to increase your output. No one really expects to stay at the level of one small unit of output per day. But there is one experience that tends to insure that you'll increase your output, one experience that makes increases in quotas unnecessary. That is the experience of *momentum*.

As I mentioned earlier, the one-small-unit quota mainly serves me during the initial phases of my writing endeavors, when I need some help in getting started. Once I get going, momentum takes over. A habit pattern is established, and I don't feel as great a need to continue thinking in terms of one small unit (though I still continue to do so). This experience of momentum is crucial to the effectiveness of the one-small-unit strategy. If you keep thinking small, you'll be continually jumping back into the task. You'll feel good about it. Energy will be continually flowing outward. The habit of getting things done (even small things) leads to momentum. And momentum, once it gets started, causes everything else to fall in line behind the task or goal. Once momentum takes over, you continue to increase the amount of work you get done. Soon you don't even *have* to think small because momentum is so great you just do your work without thinking. But you're always free to fall back upon the one-small-unit method when momentum lags.

THINKING SMALL AND ENERGY OUTPUT: A SUMMARY AND AN ANECDOTE

A common objection to this practice of "thinking small" is something like this: "If all I had to do was one small unit a day, I would just put it off until the last minute. I would be even more likely to procrastinate." Perhaps for some people that is so. This method may not work optimally for everyone. But I can say that it has worked like a charm for me. I'm less likely to procrastinate now because I have nothing to fear from large projects. It's easy to get up and do something right away. Why put it off? I now actually enjoy doing those hard tasks, such as writing, that I used to dread. You are not likely to procrastinate over anything you really enjoy doing. And that's the purpose of the "thinking small" method: to make you enjoy doing those tasks you used to dread. From the standpoint of energy and motivation, the goal is to make you *want* to do it—not just force you to complete a task you dislike, while you kick and fight all the way.

Another advantage of the "thinking small" method is that it frees up energy that would have been wasted in conflict. I now find that I have more energy for other things than I used to. When I "thought big," I used up a lot of energy just fighting myself to get started. I fight that battle much less often now. So the energy I used to use up in self-battle is now freed for other tasks.

One final illustration may help you understand how this works. A wife wants her husband to use part of his day off from work to do something for her, let's say to change the oil in her car. He gets up, thinks about doing it, and immediately experiences that sinking feeling in the pit of his stomach. That feeling indicates that an internal battle is going on—a conflict in which he is resisting the task. He has already lost some energy without even having done anything. He switches on the TV and gets wrapped up in that. But during the commercial he thinks about it again. There is another sinking feeling, this time accompanied by an almost imperceptible shudder—more energy is wasted. Soon it's time for breakfast. He thinks about it some more while he's eating. After breakfast he slowly forces himself to dress and drags himself to the garage. After kicking around a few tools, he finds the oil cans and, in a state of irritation, performs the task.

Now a different scenario—the same husband, the same task on his day off. But this time he has broken the task down into very small units. He did this the night before, while watching TV. After getting up, he thinks in terms of the first small unit: getting the jack out of the trunk. He will not allow himself to think further than that. That's all he has to do as far as he's concerned. So when he gets up at 9:15, he thinks about the one small task. It's so easy that he feels exhilarated at the thought of immediate success. After dressing and shaving, it's 9:25. There's a program he wants to watch on TV at 9:30, but the task is so easy he decides to finish it before sitting down. After getting the jack out (which takes all of two minutes), he decides to get the cans of oil (step #2). He also does task #3—open oil cans. He comes back in to watch his program. During the commercial, he decides to get task #4 out of the way, so he goes out into the garage and jacks up the car. He comes back in, finishes watching his program, and eats breakfast. After breakfast he decides to do the next task. But once he gets started—once he gets some momentum going— he just finishes the entire task. Let's say that both men finish at the same time. The latter has still been more effective because he hasn't wasted energy, the task has been rewarding, and he's enjoyed himself while doing the same things the first man hated.

Sound simplistic? Try it yourself on the next (motivationally) difficult project you despise.

USE TIME EFFICIENTLY

Dost thou love life? Then do not squander time, for that is the stuff life is made of.—Benjamin Franklin

Eternity itself cannot restore the loss struck from the minute.—Ancient poem

I wasted time, and now doth time waste me.— Shakespeare

Believe me when I tell you that thrift of time will repay you in after life with a usury of profit beyond your most sanguine dreams, and that

waste of it will make you dwindle alike in
intellectual and moral stature beyond your darkest
reckoning.—*William E. Gladstone*

*Lost! Somewhere between sunrise and sunset,
two golden hours, each set with sixty diamond
minutes. No reward is offered, for they are gone
forever.*—*Horace Mann*

*The great rule of moral conduct is, next to God,
to respect time.*—*Johann Lavater*

*Much may be done in those little shreds and
patches of time, which every day produces, and
which most men throw away, but which
nevertheless will make at the end of it no small
deduction from the life of man.*—*John Cotton*

The wisdom of the ages combines to tell us that
time is the essence of life. How we use time
constitutes a large part of the effectiveness with
which we use energy. Those who waste time
waste energy. Those who make good use of time
make good use of energy.

Procrastination is the great enemy of time, and
by minimizing procrastination you automatically
maximize time usage. One of the nicest advantages of thinking small is that it encourages you
to always be busy. As a result of small thinking,
I'm always doing something. Even when I watch
TV, I'll grab a book with the intention of reading
only one sentence. Sometimes, if the program is
good (which is rare nowadays), that is all I'll end
up reading, which is fine. But at other times I'll
read a page or two or three during the program
and get so involved or interested in the topic of
the book that I'll read an entire chapter or two

after the program is over. Before, when I thought big, planned to read an entire chapter (after all, why even begin reading if you don't plan to make it worthwhile?), I would more than likely decide to wait until the program was over before I began reading. Valuable time and momentum were lost.

Another contributor to lost time is poor planning. Too many people begin each day with no clear conception of what they need to do and how they should do it during the day. The best antidote to this tendency is to make a list of the things you want to get done that day. Probably the best time to make such a list is the night before. Then the next morning you'll be able to plunge right into the first task without delay. This gives you momentum and makes you more efficient during the remainder of the day, as your early morning activity (or inactivity) tends to determine how you will work during the remainder of the day.

Two principles should be considered as you make out your list of planned activities. In the first place, it's a good idea to place your most difficult activities at the head of the list. This means that you start on the hardest tasks in the early morning. That is when your energy and feelings of optimism are likely to be at their highest. And the good feelings that ensue from having successfully started on the most difficult task first generally give you a big enough lift in confidence to get you through the remainder of the day. There are two amendments to this statement, though. In the first place, not everyone experiences his greatest energy in the morning. Some people are afternoon types, and others are evening types. These people might want to do the most difficult tasks during periods other than the morning. (Keep in mind, though, if you are an afternoon or evening type, that doing the most difficult task in the morning has another advantage—that of boosting your confidence during the remainder of the day.)

In the second place, there may be certain tasks on which you work best by doing the easy parts first and getting them out of the way. I've noticed that if I have a technical book to read, and some of the chapters are easy while others are difficult, I do more enthusiastic reading when I start on the easy chapters first, so that I can get them out of the way. The thought of having several hard chapters *plus* an entire book to read is sometimes too much for me. Once I get all the easy chapters read, then I tend to think, "Well, there are only three (or however many) chapters left and then I'll be finished with the entire thing." This thought makes it easier for me to tackle the difficult chapters.

The second principle to keep in mind when making out your list is the old standby: Make sure you break the tasks down into their smallest possible units, especially the more difficult ones. Then when you get up in the morning, make a conscious effort to avoid thinking beyond the first small unit. After you've completed that, you can think of the second small unit. Or you can jump to another task, and come back to the second small unit later. By doing this, you keep busy *and* you avoid an energy-depleting struggle with yourself (or the energy-depleting tendency to punish yourself for not doing the difficult task you know you *should* be doing).

A third reason why people waste time is the failure to make use of small opportunities—of small units of time. There is a strong temptation in many of us to think, "If I can't finish the entire thing, or if I can't at least get the major part of it done, why begin on it at all?" The problem is that the time to do the major part of any task rarely comes. We have other things to do; sudden crises interrupt us, demanding our immediate attention, no matter what else we are doing; and our days are filled with many small snatches of time that are so short we couldn't possibly do the major part of a difficult task. How we use these small snatches of time determines, to a large extent, how efficiently we use our energy.

Consider the following:

Harriet Beecher Stowe wrote *Uncle Tom's Cabin* during snatches of time taken in between her household duties.

Longfellow translated the *Inferno* during the ten-minute period each day in which he waited for his coffee to boil, taking years to complete the task.

Madame de Genlis, who was tutor to the Queen of France, wrote several volumes of verse while waiting for the Queen to arrive for her daily lessons.

John Stuart Mill did some of his best writing while working as a clerk in the East India House.

Galileo did many of his world-shattering experiments during spare moments taken from his job as a surgeon.

Charles C. Frost became one of the world's greatest mathematicians as a result of the one hour per night he set aside for nothing but self-improvement reading.

Grote wrote his excellent *History of Greece* during small moments of time taken from his job as a banker.

George Stephenson learned arithmetic during small snatches of time found during his job as an engineer.

Henry Kirke White taught himself Greek while walking to and from the lawyer's house at which he was studying law.

Mathew Hale wrote *Contemplations* while making his rounds as a circuit judge.

So you see, small moments of time provide great opportunities for productive energy usage.

Another time-waster (and energy-waster as well) is the habit of trying to do (or think about) more than one thing at a time. Even the most energetic and talented people in the world still have this in common with the rest of us: they can only do one thing at a time. Many people go through their daily routine thinking about all the many things they have to get done. They get up in the morning and immediately begin fretting about the many demands they face. They run the list of tasks through their minds, all the while experiencing ever greater feelings of anxiety, ever more compelling feelings of pressure. They can't throw themselves completely into one task for worrying over all the other ones.

This is a bad habit to fall into. For one thing, it depletes energy. Thinking about all the many things you have to get done forces too much stimulation into the brain. Soon you are operating at too high a level of cortical energy to get anything done. Valuable energy is used up. And you don't do as good a job as you could on the immediate tasks. This is because efficient work requires concentration on the one thing at a time that you can successfully do. The person who thinks beyond one small unit is wasting his energy. The key is to have your list handy (with your daily tasks broken down into small units) and refer to that if you need direction on what to do next. But as you're working, don't think beyond your immediate task. Especially avoid thinking about the entire list of tasks.

A final cause of both energy- and time-waste is the feeling that you have to be working every single minute, and if you're not working you should at least be thinking about working. In the long run this works against the most efficient use of energy and time. Everyone needs rest periods, times to suspend both activity and concentration in order to let the mind touch lightly upon relaxing and pleasant images. These periods will actually make you more efficient and productive, rather than less so.

You'd think, at first glance, that the way for industrialists to increase the productivity of workers in their plants is simply to increase the number of hours the employees work. But industrial psychologists have consistently found that there is a point, beyond which *increased time spent at work does not increase productivity and may actually lower it*. During World War II, for example, when the British were fighting their fiercest battles with the Germans, factory managers decided to switch to a twenty-four-hour-a-day, seven-day-a-week working schedule. At first, the workers responded to these expanded hours with an increase in productivity, no doubt impelled by great feelings of patriotism. Soon, however, performance began to slip. Absences from work, tardiness, and "sickness" quickly wiped out the benefits of the increased hours. Loss of motivation speeded up the process. So the factory managers began closing on Sundays again. And they found no decrease in productivity. In fact, some factories set new records for productivity.

So don't feel that you have to keep busy every single minute. Continuous effort and concentration sooner or later wear you down and make you less efficient and productive. You need periods of time during which you do absolutely nothing just as much as you need wholesome food.

FIND YOUR OWN BEST WORKING STYLE

All of us have preferred ways of working. As in selecting a spouse, one person's meat is another's poison. If you are to maximize your ability to get things done, you should decide upon a working style that is most compatible with your personality and energy level.

This task is fairly complex. You will have to resolve such questions as how you prefer to discharge energy: steadily and evenly (as is generally characteristic of women) or in shorter, more intense bursts followed by periods of inactivity (as is generally characteristic of men). There is also the issue of what type of work you prefer to do. Here again, there is a wide range of preferences. Some people prefer to work with things, others with people. Some people prefer jobs that provide one type of reward; others seek other types of rewards. Introverts, as mentioned earlier, like jobs that provide them with the opportunity to learn and grow, while extroverts like jobs that provide money and status.

I would like to approach this question of diversity from the angle of preferred working style. A person's preferred working style includes all the above characteristics plus more: the preferred mode of energy release, the preferred type of job, the preferred type of rewards, as well as such things as personality attributes. Also, every working style is associated with certain strengths and weaknesses that should be recognized if energy use is to be maximized. I couldn't possibly cover every possible preferred working style. But I will describe the two most common ones.

These two most common working styles are the obsessional style and the administrative style. These two styles correspond roughly to the introverted and extroverted personalities, respectively. The obsessional personality is more often found among introverts and the administrative style is more often found among extroverts. The strengths and weaknesses of each are described below. Again, I'm giving more attention to the obsessional (introverted) style because in today's world that is the one which seems to lead more often to energy problems. As I will show later, modern society is much more compatible with the administrative than the obsessional style. In fact, several recent books on the topic "How to Get Ahead" have specifically offered the advice to develop the administrative style and avoid the obsessional style. This is unfortunate, because people whose style is obsessional are not comfortable with the administrative style (and vice versa). It's also unfortunate because it places an overemphasis upon "getting ahead" and an underemphasis upon really enjoying your work and being good at it, no matter what it is. According to my observations, the latter experience is in the long run much more deeply satisfying than "getting ahead" or earning a large salary. Now first a look at the obsessional style.

THE OBSESSIONAL STYLE OF WORKING

To be obsessed means "to be haunted, as by a fixed idea; to be preoccupied with something." It suggests a person who tends to become absorbed with one idea or project to the exclusion of others. The obsessional personality is not usually a good administrator, executive, or manager. These jobs require that a person be able to jump from one task to another, completely different task, without suffering any loss of efficiency. But the obsessional personality prefers to remain absorbed in one task. He dislikes being distracted from that task until he's finished with it. This working style is found very often among successful inventors, scientists, researchers, and mathematicians. These jobs generally require persistence and depth of understanding. And these are two characteristic strengths of the obsessional style. Let's take a closer look at the various characteristics—both positive and negative—of the obsessional style. The approach I will take is that if your best working style is obsessional, you should not try to change to a different style. But rather you should develop the strengths and overcome the weaknesses associated with that style. This is different from the usual advice you read, which advocates that you acquire a completely different style.

Here are the characteristics of the obsessional style:

1. *Persistence.* Obsessional personalities have long been known for their persistence. Think of Thomas Edison (a textbook obsessional) working for years in his laboratory on the light bulb, proceeding despite one failure after another on that one task until he was successful. Think also of Henry Ford, working on the automobile for days, rarely even bothering to come out of his workshop, his wife bringing him his meals (which he didn't always eat). Think also of Alex Haley, boring in on his ancestry, persistently pursuing the seemingly impossible task of tracing his genealogy, all the while allowing his rent to go

unpaid and bills to pile up unopened. All these men preferred the obsessional style of working. All were extremely persistent, one-track workers, but less effective administrators.

In the past, most of the books written on "How to Succeed" have in one form or another advocated the obsessional style. Carlyle wrote, "The weakest living creature, by concentrating his powers on a single object, can accomplish something; whereas the strongest, by dispersing his over many, may fail to accomplish anything. The drop, by continually falling, bores its passage through the hardest rock. The hasty torrent rushes over it with hideous uproar and leaves no trace behind."

Even as late as the first part of the twentieth century, the attitude prevailed that obsessional concentration and persistence at one task were the keys to effective working habits. In 1917, Orison Marden wrote a popular book entitled *Pushing to the Front.* In it he observed that, "The giants of the race have been men of concentration, who have struck sledge-hammer blows in one place until they have accomplished their purpose. The successful men of today are men of one overmastering idea, one unwavering aim, men of single and intense purpose. 'Scatteration' is the curse of American business life. Too many are like Douglas Jerrold's friend, who could converse in twenty-four languages, but had no ideas to express in any of them."[3]

That was yesterday. Today "scatteration" has become the preferred pattern of working among businessmen. As David Riesman, in his book *The*

Lonely Crowd, pointed out, increasingly the way to get to the top today is to learn a little bit about a lot of things rather than a lot about one thing. This comes from the need in bureaucracies for people who can manage other people, rather than people who have a lot of information in some area. This means that the obsessional working style may be a hindrance to those who want to "get to the top."

Even formal schooling may sometimes interfere with the obsessional style of working. In their excellent study of temperament in children, New York University psychiatrists Alexander Thomas and Stella Chess found a type of child they called "persistent."[4] These children were extremely obsessional (in the sense in which I'm using the term) in both their work and play habits. Once something captured their interest, they would stick with it until finished or satiated. Sometimes this could mean hours. One child spent several hours learning how to tie his shoes, and then a few more hours practicing his newly learned skill.

As a result of having been one of those persistent, obsessional children, I can tell you first hand that much energy is lost over the struggle. School was an upsetting, frustrating experience for me. And it took me over twenty years to find out why: My very nature rebels against the practice of dropping a task before it's been completed (or while energy and interest in it are still high) in favor of a brand new task. I haven't changed any over that twenty-year period either. I still pursue one task or project obsessively until it's finished. This is the way I work best. I may never be the president of a corporation, but I'll be happy and contented with the work I do.

If your preferred working style is obsessional, recognize that your preferred method of working is to pursue one task until it's completed. Even if your job demands that you perform a variety of different tasks, you can still adapt them to your preferred working style. One businessman makes all his phone calls on one day, writes all his reports on another, etc. One obsessional housewife washes and irons on one day, makes bread and shops on another, writes letters on the third, works in the yard on the fourth, cleans the house on the fifth, and cooks for the weekend on the sixth. Each works best when he or she can think in terms of only one task or project per day.

2. *Perfectionism.* Obsessionals are perfectionists. They have extremely high standards, and they usually punish themselves when they depart from those standards. Often this makes them excellent workers. You want your accountant, dentist, or doctor (jobs that attract obsessionals) to be a perfectionist. But almost without an exception, when I find an obsessional who is not getting his work done, who is allowing new work to pile up on his desk, or who is losing interest in a field of endeavor or a project he used to show enthusiasm for, it is because his desire for perfection has dampened his enthusiasm for the task. In its most vivid form, this can be seen in the person who engages in endless preparation for a task but never actually begins working at it.

65

Some people have spent years preparing for a career only to feel that they need to go back to school and prepare even more; in extreme cases they may never begin the career. Their entire lives may be spent in preparation.

At other times perfectionism leads to a fear of being evaluated, and an inability to meet deadlines. This was true of one of my students, Fred Lyons. His work, when he finally turned it in, was always of the highest quality—well thought out, creative, and insightful. And Fred was an aggressive thinker, someone who was rarely satisfied with a superficial understanding of subject matter. Instead, he would subject everything he read to a thorough analysis, often coming up with even better ideas than the experts who wrote the textbooks. Because he had such creative thoughts, I encouraged him to write his ideas on paper and send them in for publication. But even the mention of writing terrified Fred. For the same perfectionism that made him such a creative thinker also gave him a fear of writing things down. Anything written on paper is there for everyone to see and evaluate. And perfectionists fear being evaluated; they fear having people see that their work falls short of perfection. Fred's perfectionism made him a poorer student. He was so afraid of committing his ideas to paper that he had to constantly struggle with procrastination. As a result, his work was rarely turned in on time. This caused him to get lower grades.

So Fred Lyons combined the best and worst

features of the obsessional style: great depth of thinking and effort along with extreme perfectionism. He admitted to me one time in my office that one reason he couldn't meet deadlines was because he could only concentrate on one thing at a time. He usually kept up in one of his classes, but in the other two he suffered. "When I was an undergraduate student," he told me, "I was taking a pre-med major. The pressure was tremendous. I could only effectively concentrate on one subject at a time. But we had to take several in order to pass. The pressure finally got to me so bad that one day in class, I collapsed; I even fell out of my chair and had to be taken to the hospital. I was out of school for weeks. Even today I get anxious when more than one major task at a time is placed on my shoulders."

As far as the educational system goes, some new alternatives could be devised that are more compatible with the obsessional style. It's interesting to note that some schools have begun an experimental program in which students can take one course at a time for three or four weeks instead of three courses at a time for one quarter. This method, if it becomes popular, should help the obsessional student. But in the meantime, the obsessional can make some helpful changes in his working style. To combat procrastination, he can use some of the techniques—such as thinking small—advocated in the beginning of this chapter. He can also work on one thing only on one day. And in order to handle his perfectionistic tendencies, he can be satisfied with good work instead of perfect work. He can practice working just a little bit below his maximum.

San Diego State University has consistently produced some of the world's greatest track teams. When asked to describe the sort of teaching techniques he uses in order to be so consistently successful, the coach replied, "I just tell them to run at four fifths speed. If you try to do your very best the muscles tense and you lose energy. They practice working just a little below their maximum effort." Every perfectionistic obsessional could profit from that advice.

3. *Concern for Accuracy and Detail.* In part because of their high standards, and in part because of their alertness, obsessionals have an excellent ability to attend to details, and to do accurate, conscientious work. Another of my students, Ward Robinson, demonstrated the typical sharpness and precision of the obsessional personality. He was the sort of student who could easily enliven a classroom. The questions he asked, and the issues he raised, usually led to lively discussions. His pinpoint thinking generally caused his professors to watch their words and not make any statements they couldn't back up. For Ward sat almost on the edge of his seat, his eyes peering alertly as his teacher talked, examining every statement intently. If the teacher left himself open, Ward would say, in a calm, but commanding manner, "But professor, if that's the case, then . . ." and proceed to nail him to the wall. Ward's main problem in the classroom was a tendency to nitpick. Sometimes he became so

wrapped up in details that he lost the overall picture. But other than that, he was almost the perfect student.

One problem is that the obsessional's concern for accuracy and detail can, if carried to an extreme, actually inhibit energy and impair optimum work habits. The obsessional often sacrifices speed for accuracy. This is great in some jobs—such as accounting. But others are better tackled with a balance between speed and accuracy. One housewife named Joan once complained to me about her inability to work as efficiently as her friends. She said, "I've noticed that Nancy seems to get more done than I do. She works a lot faster and still her work isn't less efficient."

I had observed the two together on a couple of occasions, so I replied, "The problem is that you are overconcerned with accuracy. You begin even simple tasks, like washing dishes, with too much fretfulness. You seem to fear that you won't do it right unless you really concentrate. But Nancy doesn't even think about it. She just plunges from one task to another with no fear of falling short of high standards." So in some tasks, especially routine ones, too much of an emphasis upon accuracy can cramp effort and energy.

4. *Doubting.* One final characteristic of obsessionals—and one that is strongly related to both energy use and working habits—is the tendency to doubt. Not all obsessional personalities have this characteristic, but those who do suffer from it. They have trouble making a decision, and once they do make one they go

over and over it, asking themselves, "Did I choose the right way?" The classic example of obsessional doubting is that of the person who locks all his doors, goes to bed, starts doubting that he actually locked his doors, and has to get out of bed to recheck the locks.

Writers often suffer from this type of obsessional doubting. In a recent biography of Joseph Conrad, for example, the author pointed out that Conrad used to agonize over every single sentence he wrote. When I first began to write, I experienced the same trauma. And from what I've seen and heard since then, I've concluded that many other writers suffer from the same problem. The attitude arises that there is one, and only one, way to write something. And you must search your mind until you find that one best way. In actuality there are many equally effective ways of writing the same book or performing the same task. As long as no moral issue is involved, it really doesn't matter which one you choose.

I think this tendency to doubt comes from the obsessional's overconcern with accuracy. If you believe that there is only one (perfect) way to do something, then you will always worry over whether or not you did it the right way. Get that thought out of your mind! It only serves to deplete your energy. There are several different ways of doing the same task. Everyone puts his own stamp upon work he performs. No two people do it exactly the same way, whether it's building a barn or writing a book.

So these are the strengths and weaknesses of the obsessional style of working. When properly used—the strengths maximized and the weaknesses controlled—it can be a very efficient, productive approach. It's interesting to note that the apostle Paul advocated this style for the Christian. "This one thing I do," he started one of his sentences, suggesting the obsessional's persistent preoccupation with the one overriding purpose. In another place, he compared Christian growth with running a race. And he advised Christians to practice singleness of purpose in regards to their Christian experience (as did Christ: "If therefore thine eye be single, thy whole body shall be full of light," Matt. 6:22).

One well-known psychologist wrote an article several years back in which he attributed the great economic and scientific growth of America to "obsessional protestantism."[5] The type of personality that protestantism tended to encourage was that of a thrifty, hardworking, intensely concentrating, persistent personality. That personality style was responsible for the great scientific and economic advancement made by the United States. So don't be ashamed if your style is obsessional. Recognize the great energy inherent in that style and use it to your advantage.

THE ADMINISTRATIVE WORKING STYLE

The opposite working preference from that of the obsessional—and the one that more closely corresponds to the extroverted personality—could be called the administrative style. I've chosen the term "administrative style" because it is found most often among executives and managers. These positions usually require the ability to handle several completely different tasks during the day, rather than to concentrate intensely upon one task or project. The high school principal, for example, may have to deal with disciplinary problems, parent-teacher conferences, financial statements, reports, visits from higher administrators, and toilets that don't flush—all in one day. The introverted obsessional finds these different tasks distracting from his major project. But the more extroverted administrator is usually stimulated by them. He likes to jump from one thing to the next. He usually becomes bored if he has to stick to only one task or project for a long time.

For this reason the administrative personality often appears more "energetic," in the usual sense of the word, than the obsessional. He moves about more vigorously, appears more optimistic, talks more enthusiastically, is more "alive" and spontaneous in social situations, and changes activities more easily. But the obsessional has a much greater intensity of concentration on one subject. In this sense, the two styles can be compared to lights. The administrative personality is like a chandelier, with many small light bulbs in it. None of those light bulbs are very bright by themselves. But all of them together give off a good amount of light. (Each single light bulb represents an activity.) The obsessional, on the other hand, is like one larger light bulb. On the whole, it may give off no more light (energy) than the chandelier (and usually gives off much less), but the light it does give off is intense and focused, and it lights up its own smaller, more concentrated area much better than the chandelier covers its area. So the difference lies in the area and intensity of energy. The administrative personality gives off more energy, but that energy is spread out over a larger number of activities and hence is not intense at any one task. The obsessional personality usually gives off less energy, but that energy is restricted to fewer areas. And the intensity of energy is much greater within those few areas. The fact that these two working styles correspond closely to extroversion and introversion is witnessed in the research which shows that administrators and managers tend to have extroverted personalities, while scientists and technicians tend to have introverted personalities.

But the most important thing is for each of us to find and utilize our own best working style. Both styles are necessary. Neither style has anything to be ashamed of. In fact, your best bet is to cultivate your preferred style to its maximum, not pine away for a different style.

NOTES

1. Marie Ray, *How Never to Be Tired* (Indianapolis, IN: Bobbs-Merrill, 1938).
2. William James, *Pragmatism* (New York: New American Library, 1965).
3. Orison Marden, *Pushing to the Front* (New York: The Success Company, 1911).

4. Alexander Thomas and Stella Chess, *Temperament and Development* (New York: Brunner/Mazel, 1977).
5. George Albee, "The Protestant Ethic, Sex and Psychotherapy," *American Psychologist*, February, 1977.

CHAPTER THREE
ENERGY BARRIERS:
HOW TO OVERCOME THEM

We've all been through experiences and mental
states that made us feel unenergetic. These
experiences prevent us from using our energy
appropriately. Often they indicate that it's time
to change some habits or switch activities.
Surprisingly, some of these so-called energy
barriers can actually serve to energize you, if you
know how to use them. This is especially true of
guilt and tension. Others, such as fatigue, are
more consistent drains on energy. Let's take a look
at these energy barriers—their causes, effects,
and some advice on how to overcome them.

DEPRESSION

Depression is rapidly becoming one of the most
prevalent disturbances in the United States. It's
estimated that at any given time over eight
million people in the United States are severely

depressed, to the point of being in need of psychiatric help. The number of people less severely depressed, yet still hurting, is no doubt even larger.

The negative features of depression are obvious: the experience of pain and passivity, feelings of helplessness, lowered self-esteem, etc. All this makes life seem unrewarding. Energy is depleted right along with the joy of living. As will become clearer later on, depression is closely tied in with a faulty use of aggressive energy. Relief from depression sometimes depends upon a positive outflow of aggressive energy. It is also important, in dealing with depression, to realize that it can have positive as well as negative features.

Point out to most depressed persons that a large percentage of highly gifted and creative individuals were very susceptible to depressions, and it will probably have little sway with them. But it's still true that depressions appear to occur disproportionately among the gifted and sensitive. Depression is also adaptive in that it provides quite an opportunity for growth if it is used correctly. And this is the whole secret of dealing with depression: not so much avoiding depression as learning to utilize it adaptively.

Signs of Depression. Most depressed people undergo a *lowering of spirits*. Though this experience will vary from person to person, it usually consists of some of the following feelings: pain, crying spells, sadness, loss of interest in anything, fright, hopelessness, lack of self-confidence, drop in self-esteem, inability to experience happiness or satisfaction with anything. Usually the depressed person has a feeling of being trapped; in his own eyes there is no way out of his situation, no matter how obvious the solution to his problems looks to an objective eye.

Withdrawal from social contact is common among depressed people. Even normally gregarious individuals, when depressed, tend to avoid others. They don't necessarily want to be alone (because depressed people are often intensely lonely); they just seem to fear being rejected and insulted by others. So they avoid people who might help them. It's a sad thing, but the dejected manner of the depressed person often does make others avoid him. This appears to him to be rejection. And this rejection he fears intensely because it further lowers his self-esteem.

There is usually a *drop in motivation and energy.* The depressed individual typically finds it hard to perform even the simplest and most routine tasks. Complicated procedures apparently would deplete him, at least in his own eyes. His very movements slow down until he appears retarded in speech and activity. He moves about slowly and painstakingly and speaks in a very slow fashion. In fact, on psychological tests, one of the first signs of an imminent depression is a slowing down of reaction time and a lengthening of the period of time it takes to administer the test.

Sleep disturbances are frequent. These usually

take two forms: In one the depressed person has trouble falling asleep and in the other he tends to awaken early in the morning before it's time to get up. There is some evidence that the latter indicates a more serious form of depression than the former. But in any event the tendency of the depressed person is to lie in bed stewing over problems instead of sleeping.

A *lowered sexual drive* is also common among depressed individuals. It could be that sexual energy is rechanneled into efforts to cope with the lowered mood and thus isn't available for day-to-day activities. Or it could be that depression brings about a general decline in energy level. In either case little energy is left for less vital (to the depressed individual) functions, such as sexual activities.

A *loss of appetite* also often accompanies loss of sexual interest. "Even the best food tastes like sawdust to me," complained one depressed individual. As a result the depressed individual sometimes loses weight. Some—a small minority—go to the other extreme, though; they overeat until they actually gain weight. In fact, these persons may respond to depression by oversleeping and engaging in compulsive sexual experiences, as well as overeating.

Sometimes *anxiety and tension* occur in a depression. In fact, any person undergoing an anxious, tense state, especially if it lasts for a long period of time, may be suspected of having a depression even if no other signs of depression are present.

Acute Versus Chronic Depressions. One useful dimension of depression is the acute-chronic continuum. Acute depressions are usually reactions to some specific event such as a death in the family. The person experiencing an acute depression will tend to go through a phase of sadness and then eventually come out of the depression. Acute depressions don't respond to drugs or electroconvulsive shock, and their symptoms are milder than those of the second group, chronic depressions.

The chronic depressions seem to result from some internal, unconscious process. They last longer than acute depressions and a specific cause is harder to identify. Research indicates that chronic depressions respond to drug treatment and shock therapy. And there is some evidence that there are genetic predispositions to chronic depressions. In any event, a chronic depression is more severe and long-lasting than an acute depression, and it takes less to set off a chronic depression.

Origins. The following are the most frequent causes of depression. Specific causes vary from person to person, some individuals being more susceptible to one cause than to another.

1. The most frequent cause of depression is that of *loss.* Studies have shown that depressions often follow the loss of a loved one; and people who during childhood experienced the loss of a parent through death, divorce, or separation are much more susceptible to depressions as adults

than individuals who grew up in a united home. One study found that almost half of the adult subjects undergoing a severe depression had, as children, suffered the loss of a parent. In another study on adolescent attempted suicides, it was revealed that almost half had lost a parent earlier in life. This is powerful evidence in support of the biblical plan for marriage and the biblical injunction against divorce. In fact, as I'll point out later, a loving home background is one of the best contributors to a high energy level and freedom from depression.

You don't have to lose a loved one in order to become depressed, though. A loss of values can produce the same results. Cross-cultural research indicates that many depressions occur among citizens of societies that are in the process of losing their value systems. This is increasingly becoming a problem in our society. People are uncertain of their values, of their standards of conduct. Many values that we have cherished in the past are now being called into question, usually by persons who see those values as impediments to their "freedom." Individuals with sensitive consciences, with high standards of responsibility, are coming to sense a great loss due to these lowered standards. The loss, and consequent depression, becomes even more likely if that person violates his own standards despite protests from his conscience. One of the most important problems that faces Americans today is a clarification of their values. This would be one effective way of stopping the tremendous increase in depressions witnessed over the last decade.

You may also become depressed as a result of the loss of a goal. Some people experience a depression when their efforts to attain a highly prized goal are unsuccessful. Some people set themselves up for depressions when they set goals that are unrealistically high. In these cases the depression can be lifted either when the person comes to believe again that his goals are attainable or when his goals are either modified to become realistic or relinquished altogether. One young man experienced recurring depressions as a result of his frustrated attempts to become an artist, a goal that was very unrealistic for him. He couldn't be satisfied until he lowered his sights and concentrated on painting for enjoyment rather than fame.

2. Depression and personality. Some personalities are more susceptible to depression than others. The susceptible personality usually possesses the following characteristics:

Dependency. Psychoanalysts say that depressed people tend to develop overly strong feelings of dependency; they lose too much of themselves in their loved ones. When the loved one leaves, whether temporarily or permanently, a feeling of rage is experienced. But because the person cannot express his rage, it lies dormant, and the depressed person turns the anger inward on himself. Aggressive energy is stirred up and then blocked. Sometimes this can lead to suicide.

Some people respond to unmet dependency needs by seeking promiscuous, impersonal sexual relationships. The person with low self-esteem often finds it exciting when someone else manifests sexual desire for him. This is especially true of depressed women. They can often be drawn into sexual relationships that lack long-term commitment. This is only likely to increase the intensity of their depression, although they may experience a temporary upswing in mood. But the depression has not been squarely dealt with; it's still there. And once the excitement of the new sexual experience has worn off, it will become even more painful than before. This seems to be a common experience among individuals in the "sexual revolution" generation. Sexuality, when it is so free, becomes depersonalized. It loses its individuality. Depression ensues. On the other hand, sexuality within the frame of a long-term commitment— through marriage—can be intensely rewarding and can even counteract depression if the marriage is a stable one. In fact, no other relationship will have so much influence upon the depressed adult as his marital relationship. Every effort should be made to maintain marital stability and insure long-term commitments. To do otherwise is to engender the sort of helplessness and instability that lead to depression.

The depressed personality usually has *trouble expressing anger and hostility.* As a result, aggressive energy has a way of building up inside and turning against the self. For one reason or another the depressed person soon fails to use his aggressive energy in his work, or to aid the pursuit of his goals. This failure increases his feelings of helplessness and that in turn increases his depression. Often he can only be relieved of his depression when he once again comes to feel that he has some control over his environment. And this control depends to a large extent upon aggressive energy.

According to psychiatrist Frederick Flach, the following characteristics are also found among depression-prone individuals:

May appear self-preoccupied but does care for other people.

Strong need to be liked and respected.

Dependent on those he loves.

Somewhat rigid and inflexible.

Highly sensitive to the way others treat him.

Has a need to control his environment.

Comes from or is currently enmeshed in an environment—home or work—that does not encourage the free expression of feelings.

These personality characteristics suggest that introverts are more prone to depression than extroverts. Introverts generally develop intensive friendships with and become dependent on just a few people. Extroverts on the other hand, are more dependent upon the group. So the introverted person is likely to experience a deeper sense of sadness when a loved one is lost.

Also, introverts have stricter consciences and a greater sense of responsibility than extroverts. They are more likely to be self-critical and self-evaluative, both of which are often associated with depressions.

Helplessness and Depression. Whenever you reach the point of believing that you are no longer in control of your life, you are susceptible to a depression. This belief is called "helplessness." It's been observed in laboratory animals, in humans who die from "voodoo death," and in people who are undergoing a depression. When a person acquires a mental state of helplessness, three reactions follow. First, his motivation to act declines. He thinks, "What's the use?" He just doesn't feel like doing anything. Second, he loses his expectations of success. In other words, he comes to feel that even if he does act, his actions will likely end in failure. Third, his level of emotional arousal increases. He feels tense, anxious, agitated, But since he expects failure and is unmotivated to act, the emotional energy is not used to enhance creativity or productivity. Instead it turns inward and makes him feel uncomfortable.

The energy-depleting effects of a sense of helplessness are evident anytime a human or animal loses control over its environment. This is clearly evident among animals who are taken from their natural habitats and placed in zoos. They will sit and watch their food wilt on the floor without eating it. This is especially true of monkeys and apes. But when these animals are given control over their feeding—when, for example, they have to push a lever after a light comes on in order to receive food—they will show an amazing recovery of energy, spirit, and appetite.

Probably the most dramatic evidence of the effects of helplessness are seen in so-called "voodoo deaths." The American physiologist W. B. Cannon was the first scientist to study voodoo deaths. He was able to witness firsthand what took place among superstitious people after a "curse" had been placed upon them. In Brazil he watched an Indian who had been condemned to die by his medicine man. The Indian sat down, and in a state of helpless passivity died within hours. In Africa, a young black man was cursed to die after it was discovered that he ate a forbidden food. His strong emotional reaction of fear and anxiety were turned inward by his sense of helplessness, and within twenty-four hours he was dead.

Cannon's description of the usual way these people react is alarmingly illustrative of the effects of extreme helplessness. The cursed person "stands aghast with his eyes staring" at the cursing instrument (sometimes a stick or a bone). He raises his hand in an attempt to protect himself from the lethal poison he believes is seeping into his body. "His cheeks blanch, and his eyes become glassy, and the expression of his face becomes horribly distorted." He tries to cry out, but his voice is paralyzed from fear. A foamy froth, rather than words, emerges from his mouth. His body begins to shake and tremble uncontrollably. He sways back and forth, and then falls to the ground. Eventually he regains enough self-control to pick himself up and walk back to his hut. There he soon frets his life away.

This same experience of helplessness-resulting-in-a-loss-of-energy occurs among depressed people in this country, only on a much less intense level. At least that is what one psychologist has discovered. Martin Seligman has conducted numerous studies on the phenomenon of helplessness, and he's written a book on the subject entitled *Helplessness*.[1] Based upon his studies, Seligman concluded that a feeling of helplessness is one of the major contributors to the experience of depression. He proposes that if the main contributor to a feeling of helplessness is the attitude that your actions will not make a difference, then the way to cure helplessness is to reverse that expectation; that is, to help the depressed person feel that he has gained some control over his environment. This sounds ridiculously simple; but experiments show that animals in whom helplessness has been engendered usually require very directive retraining in order to recapture the attitude of competence.

The same holds true for humans. In one study, for example, children were required to work on several unsolvable arithmetic problems; after a short while they were then given solvable problems. The researchers discovered that these children were unable to solve the solvable problems, which were well within their competence, as long as these problems were given to them by the same teachers who had given them the unsolvable problems. The solvable problems had to be presented to the children by new teachers in order for success to be experienced.

So, for the person who has come to believe that he can't exercise control over his environment, drastic changes often have to be brought about: changes in the environment, changes in his mental set, and changes in the coping strategies he typically employs.

One way in which this can be achieved is to break down difficult tasks into very small units and have the depressed person tackle the task one small unit at a time. This method was explained in chapter two. It is a very effective method for getting energy flowing outward. Seligman cites one experiment in which a group of very depressed persons were first required to read a paragraph aloud (this may sound ludicrously simple to the average individual, but depressions often are debilitating to the point that even a simple task such as this one becomes difficult). Next they were required to read a different paragraph and then interpret it; the following step was to read another paragraph, interpret it, and then argue the author's point of view. Finally, the depressed person was given three topics and asked to make a speech out of them. The result was that most of these individuals showed pronounced mood lifts. Once their energy flow was reestablished and they gained the attitude that they could be successful (even if it were just at a simple task such as that one), the depression lifted.

Sometimes the depressed person needs to realize that he is responsible for his successes and failures. Many people grow up to believe that they are not responsible for their own successes and failures. In one study, for example, children who gave up easily on arithmetic problems were trained to attribute their failure to complete difficult arithmetic problems to their own lack of effort. (They were told, after failing to complete these impossible arithmetic problems, "You didn't try hard enough.") Another group was given only problems on which they could succeed. The group that was given the impossible problems and trained to attribute their failure to their own lack of effort improved when they were given realistic problems. The second group, the one given easy problems only, continued to go to pieces after failures.

I'm not advocating that we purposefully make things rough. Individuals who are in a state of helplessness need patience and understanding; but they also need encouragement in overcoming obstacles, not removal of the obstacles. In fact, forced exposure to a situation that requires active mastery may be one of the best ways of breaking up a helpless depression. For example, in the Tuscaloosa plan, practiced by a Veterans Administration Hospital in Alabama, depressed people are put in an antidepression room. Here they are exposed to a taskmaster who requires them to perform simple tasks such as sanding a block of wood. They begin sanding it. The taskmaster criticizes them for sanding it against the grain; next he criticizes them for sanding it with the grain. This criticism continues until finally the depressed person, in exasperation, says something like, "Get off my back," or "I'm not doing this anymore," at which time he is immediately let out of the room with apologies and allowed to go his own way. What these individuals are learning is that they can exercise control over their environments with the mechanism of aggressive energy—through self-assertion. Experiments have shown that this plan breaks up depression quickly.

Depression and Growth. There seems to be a relationship between susceptibility to depression and creativity. Many creative people have been highly prone to depressions. Consider the following cases:

Sir Winston Churchill was so susceptible to depression that he even came up with names for his various depressions.

Jonathan Swift, author of *Gulliver's Travels,* was so pessimistic and depression-prone that he dressed in black on his birthdays as a symbol of mourning his existence.

John Stuart Mill, the British genius, responsible in part for the modern scientific method of investigation, reported that, "I have not seen one happy day in all of my life."

Creative people are often sensitive and depression-prone. But depression is correlated with creativity in another sense. In order to grow, in order to break out of old patterns of thinking, we must first experience a stage of depression. As Frederick Flach puts it in his book, *The Secret Strength of Depression:* "The majority of creative people, whether the term 'creativity' is used in the narrow, artistic sense or in the broader sense of being able to see things in a fresh way and to combine concepts in an original manner, will attest to the fact that they have experienced significant episodes of acute depression from which they have rebounded to reach new levels of creativity."[2] Flach goes on to say that acute depressions are often necessary to help people see things from a different perspective and thus to free them from past habits or to get them out of a rut. Emerging from a depression thus resembles breaking water after you've been submerged for a long time. The fresh air is exhilarating.

Viewed from this perspective, depressions are both an opportunity for growth and a necessary step in the process of growth. Those who are unable to experience and face squarely the pain of depression, with every intent of coming out of it stronger, will be unlikely to share in the process of growth. Anyone who is attempting to change his life situation for the better will more than likely have to undergo at least mild depressions. In fact, many existentialists have adopted the position that the "night of gloom" in which the feelings of emptiness and pain are experienced and confronted squarely are the only ways in which growth and personality adjustment can be achieved.

The following are suggestions for learning to use depressions as they should be used: as steps in the process of growth.

1. Face the depression squarely; don't always attempt to dodge it by such maneuvers as thinking positive thoughts. This is not an easy task. Most people would rather be in a state of ecstasy or euphoria all the time. Books on how to be happy sell rapidly because they seem to be saying that adjustment can be attained by such simple remedies as thinking positive thoughts. And a positive mental framework is important

for living a full life. But confronting pain and mastering it are also important, and they are usually underemphasized.

The poorest response to depression is a bout of pleasure-seeking activities. But unfortunately this is a common reaction. Rather than spending a period of time alone, attempting to master their pain, many individuals will go on a bout of drinking, drugs, promiscuity, and entertainment-seeking in order to avoid the very experience that would make them stronger. Unfortunately for them, once the entertainment is over, once they've come down from the high, once the sexual activity is completed, they will still be faced with the depression, and it will probably be stronger and more intense than before.

As I see it, a successful depression, one from which you emerge stronger than before, goes through at least two stages. The first stage is the initial agitation and lowering of mood. During this initial stage you should confront the depression squarely by asking yourself tough questions such as, "What could have caused this depression?" "Am I the sort of person who is likely to become depressed?" "Has someone been rude to me lately?" "Have I lost something?" "Am I living up to my own standards?" By experiencing a depression face-to-face and attempting to work through it, we often deal with it once and for all. But if we attempt to run from it by pleasure-seeking or dodge it by thinking positive thoughts, we may not be dealing with the conditions that created it in the first place. Even if we are successful in temporarily elevating our mood, the conditions that caused it in the first place are still there. The depression will simply lurk beneath the surface, often for years, siphoning off our energy and giving us a vague sense of unpleasantness.

After having experienced the depression and confronted it with such questions as those listed above, the next step is to pull yourself out of the depression. I think it's important for a person to exercise control over the entire process of depression. I think it's important for him, once he feels depressed, to confront it (or at least the conditions that may have created it). Then the next step is for him to actively bring himself out of it. The advantage of actively experiencing it and then actively conquering it is that this promotes a feeling of control and thereby wards off feelings of helplessness. The person who passively allows the depression to lead his feelings wherever it may will be giving up his self-control and enhancing the likelihood that he will feel helpless. Even if we are prone to experience depressions, by learning how to actively bring ourselves out of them we enhance our own spirit of competence and we experience a feeling of growth and strength.

2. Avoid procrastination. It's a small point, but I find that when people frequently procrastinate they increase their chances of feeling helpless and depressed. Often the longer we put off activities that are important to us, the stronger will be our sense of helplessness. So one sure way of increasing your feeling of competence is to simply force yourself to jump right into a task that you

feel tempted to put off. This is a good way to end a depression even if the procrastination did not engender it.

3. Learn to channel aggressiveness into productive activity. Aggressiveness, if it is not sublimated and worked off, will tend to turn inward on you, engendering self-punitiveness and low self-esteem. And one of the central problems of people predisposed toward depressions is the handling of aggressive energy. Proper self-assertiveness is an important skill for these people to learn. But frequently we are placed in situations in which self-assertion is not feasible. Criticism from a boss is an example. In these cases, we need to deal with the aroused aggression in an active manner. Productive work is probably the best response. Another excellent way of getting aggressive energy flowing outward is to write an angry letter to someone who has mistreated you. Don't hold back. Tell him everything that he's done and what you think of him. Then tear up the letter and throw it away.

4. Learn to adapt constructively to your mood swings. Some people are biologically predisposed to mood swings. Many women, for example, experience depressions and a drop in spirits during the last few days of their menstrual cycle (called the pre-menstrual syndrome). In these cases you can't tie the depression to any specific cause outside the rise and fall of hormone levels (and other as-yet-unidentified biological factors). The person simply has to live with recurrent mood swings.

For these people the best way of handling the

depression is similar to, but slightly different from, the advice given above. When a person experiences mood swings periodically, the self-confrontation and the tough questions may be unnecessary. More important is adjusting your activities to the lowered mood swing. I find that engaging in passive activities, such as reading, serves me better during down-swings in mood; I save the more active activities, such as writing, for the period when my mood is higher.

Dr. Walter C. Alvarez, in his book *Live at Peace with Your Nerves*,[3] cites his experience with a woman whose personality he called "manic-depressive"; that is, she underwent very high states of elation followed by very low periods of depression. He noted that "when she was depressed, [she] hibernated in a darkened room, and when she was manic was a wonderful hostess. At such times, she would sit up until three in the morning, talking or writing a novel." Here is an example of actively adjusting and adapting to a biological reality (mood swings), instead of passively and helplessly experiencing it.

GUILT AND SELF-CRITICISM

According to psychoanalysts, guilt is a form of anxiety or emotional energy that is used by the conscience to punish us when we've violated, or fallen short of, our standards. Over the short term, guilt is not as enervating and depleting as depression. In fact, guilt, like any other strong emotion, can actually serve as a strong source of energy and motivation. People have made massive donations to charity, walked miles to return overdue library books, and done painstaking detective work to pay back others they've wronged, all as a result of guilt. So guilt can motivate some fairly involved behaviors. But over the long run, excessive guilt in all its forms—remorse, self-criticism, and self-condemnation—serves to use up energy.

At its best, guilt should serve as an advance warning device, telling us that we're about to violate one of our standards. Psychiatrists tell us that guilt not only is aroused *after* a person has done something wrong; even the person's *intent* to act contrary to one of his own important principles elicits guilt. So if we find ourselves even *thinking* about violating a standard, some guilt should be experienced. That guilt should warn us not to further indulge any such thoughts or actions. And it should provide us with the energy necessary to resist the temptation.

Unfortunately, guilt and the conscience don't always work that efficiently. Human nature being what it is, we often experience guilt *after* we've already violated some standard or principle. We sin and then feel guilty as a result of our sin. Surprisingly, the guilt that results from the sin can serve to make future sinning more likely. This is because guilt is a form of emotional energy. And, as I point out in the chapter on "Three Sources of Energy," when our emotions are aroused during some action, those emotions cut "deep grooves" in our habit patterns. Those "deep grooves" make it more likely that we will again act in a similar manner sometime in the future.

Some psychiatrists have described this "self-punitive" guilt cycle in detail. It has two forms. In the first form, the person's transaction with himself goes like this: I'll keep punishing myself if I can continue to violate my conscience. The guilt becomes a type of penance. The person doesn't want to give up the sin even though it brings down the wrath of his conscience, so he goes through a period of self-punishment in order to relieve his conscience. Then he can sin again.

A good example of this is a married man who was having an extramarital affair that he didn't want to give up. It violated his standards. He knew he was sinning. But he still wanted to have his affair. So after each episode, he would condemn himself. He would even tell his friends what he was doing, and how low a person he was. Then he would feel purged enough to go out and do it again. Needless to say, much energy was lost in this self-defeating cycle.

In the second form of the self-punitive guilt cycle, the person's transaction with himself goes like this: I must keep punishing myself in order to undo what I've done. Here the person usually has a general sense of unworthiness, often resulting either from the sin that originally set off the guilt cycle or from a poor self-concept. The guilty, unworthy person simply confirms his unworthiness by continuing to sin. Then he inflicts punishment on himself by feeling guilty.

This cycle has been found among groupies,

young women who follow rock stars and football players around, seeking short-term sexual thrills before they are dumped. The women usually have very poor self-concepts. Their self-destructive promiscuity is simply a way of confirming their sense of worthlessness. Once emotional energy becomes wrapped up in these self-punitive guilt cycles, unwinding the process may be very difficult. Often only a deep religious conversion can break the pattern with a new type of energy: love and faith. This was what saved Mary Magdalene from her cycle of self-destruction.

Guilt shouldn't be seen as a completely negative experience, though. The conscience is the source of all self-improvement, discipline, and growth. And guilt is the source of energy with which the conscience motivates us. The current trend in psychiatry toward attacking the conscience and guilt as no longer necessary is a very destructive philosophy. Anthropologists generally differentiate between "guilt-oriented" cultures and "shame-oriented" cultures. In shame-oriented cultures people are controlled by others. Their consciences are not well developed, and they rarely (if ever) experience guilt. These shame-oriented cultures are always primitive and backward. An advanced civilization depends to a certain extent upon guilt and conscience. In a country such as America, people can't keep a close watch on one another. Individuals have to be self-controlled rather than other-controlled. And self-control always involves at least a little guilt.

So in summary, guilt is a necessary human experience. We should have high standards, and we should be able to experience some guilt before we are in danger of violating those standards—not after. Used in this way, guilt is a source of energy. It motivates us to continue growing and striving. When it's excessive, though, and when it occurs too often *after* we've sinned, it turns into an energy-depleting experience. In that case it should tell us that we need to tap into the sort of energy that only God can provide.

TENSION

Tension is another experience that, like guilt, has both positive and negative aspects. The negatives of tension are pretty obvious. Muscular tightness uses up vital energy. The muscles are contracting and using up energy for no purpose; they are putting out effort without productivity. Such tension is a waste.

Muscular tension is bad for another reason. Tense muscles often tighten up to the point that they impair the free flow of blood. Since blood is the life force, this can have devastating effects upon some organs of the body over the years. If the face is perpetually tense, it doesn't receive the proper amount of blood. Since the lack of blood can cause premature aging, this may make the tense person appear older than he is. The loss of blood because of tension often makes the feet and hands uncomfortably cold, another sign of poor circulation.

There are many different sources of tension, especially in an advanced industrialized culture. The race to get ahead, to acquire more and more, certainly qualifies as a common source of tension in today's world. Overly ambitious people are especially vulnerable to peptic ulcers, heart attacks, headaches, and the whole range of tension-induced disorders. Many are in such a hurry to get ahead that they lose the ability to relax and recover their depleted vital energy. Over a long period they can end up working on nerves alone.

Intense concentration for long periods of time may be another source of tension, especially if stress goes along with the job. This is especially true among air traffic controllers. They have to concentrate very intensely in the face of extreme pressure. One mistake could result in the loss of hundreds of lives. As a result, their vital energy reserves are soon depleted. Few last on the job for more than five or six years, at least in large airports. Anyone whose work requires intense concentration needs to learn to take frequent rest stops. But this is difficult because once a person gets into the habit of concentrating it's often hard for him to relax. If you are this sort of person, keep in mind that over the long run those rest stops will help you get more done. And they will serve to restore your energy level.

Tension is often found in jobs that don't require any physical effort. Executives and managers are especially prone to muscular tension. They are placed in situations that arouse their emotions, but they cannot work off the emotional energy through exercise. That's why health spas and gymnasiums have become necessary in order to help tense people cope with stresses.

99

Many sources of tension, such as those listed above, are results of industrialized, big-city living. But some people have predispositions toward tension. The *tense personality* is usually slim and firm, but not graceful in movement. On the contrary, he tends to be either jerky, nervous, overly reactive, and ill at ease; or he may be rigid, stiff, and almost paralyzed in appearance. Of the two types the latter is worse. At least the fidgety person works off tension and emotional energy through his nervous movements. Some people drum their fingers; others clap their hands together repeatedly; still others fidget in their chairs. People who constantly move about in this manner usually have a high level of drive—a lot of emotional energy, in other words. They should learn to relax, I agree. But I no longer believe that they should necessarily stop those nervous movements.

I first drew this conclusion based upon my own experience with nervous movements. But what I've seen and read since then has verified my initial observation. Most of the men in my family have the nervous habit of jiggling one leg up and down while they sit. A few of the more high-strung ones will also drum their fingers as they jiggle their legs. Whether this is an inherited or learned nervous movement, I can't say. But I do believe that a high level of emotional energy does run in the family. Anyway, several years ago my grandmother decided that this was a waste of energy and took it upon herself to stop it. She tried to stop her grandchildren from jiggling whenever one of them started. I was around her quite a bit at the time, so I practically stopped this nervous activity. But soon after, I noticed an increase in muscular tension both in my legs and in the back of my neck. I was able to relieve this tension only after I went back to jiggling my leg.

We have a fear, I think, about appearing nervous. It's considered bad manners—an indication of a lack of poise. But people with much emotional energy need some kind of outlet. Otherwise the tension turns inward. Perhaps we should learn to think differently about nervous movements. Instead of signifying a lack of poise, they represent deep levels of emotional energy. The nervous person has the gift of emotional energy with all its advantages (creativity, recuperative powers, intensity, and drive). One successful administrator I know is a nervous man. He seems to be almost always in motion. He listens to other people with an intense look on his face, often fidgeting with his hands as he listens. But his fidgetings somehow don't seem like the nervous movements of the hesitant, unsure person. Rather, they convey the image of a wellspring of available energy. But he also knows how to relax and conserve his energy. At various intervals during the day he sits in his chair or lies on the floor and suspends all active thought and movement. He simply relaxes completely. This practice insures that he will have enough energy to meet every task.

So there's nothing at all wrong with "nervous fidgeting," expecially if it's punctuated with periods of complete relaxation. But even during those periods of relaxation, all motor movement is not necessarily suspended. I think that some books on "How to Relax" have been less helpful than they should because they advise that all muscular movement must be stopped. One of the methods of relaxation I tried several years ago uses the verbal technique of telling your muscles to "let go." The author states that you should lie down on the floor, with pillows under your neck and knees, and cease all movement. Then, beginning with your arms (since they appear to be the easiest part of the body to relax), you should instruct your muscles to "let go" (without actually speaking) over and over again. After you've completely relaxed your arms, then you can go on to the next part of your body. Eventually you will have relaxed your entire body.

I believe that his technique of instructing the muscles to "let go" is useful, but I can't agree that you should try to stop all muscular movement and lie completely still. The chances are good that you will increase, rather than decrease, your tension if you try to lie completely still. Studies have shown that even when you enter the deepest levels of sleep, when you are very relaxed, you are not still. On the contrary, you toss and turn periodically. And if you move about during the periods of deep sleep, then certainly movement is not incompatible with relaxation. In fact, movement tends to help you relax by discharging tension and emotional energy.

I've found the following techniques of relaxation very helpful: Before you ever lie (or sit) down you should make sure that excess tension has been discharged and your muscles are ready to relax. In order to do this two procedures are helpful. The first is to breathe deeply and fully. This is one of the keys to relaxation. In fact, unless you breathe deeply and regularly, I doubt that any of the other relaxation techniques will work very well. (Sometimes deep breathing by itself, without any of the many relaxation techniques, will be enough to relax you.) The term "deep breathing" doesn't mean that you have to strain to suck as much air into your lungs as possible. That causes you to tense up, and thereby lose the benefits of breathing. It simply means that you breathe fully, slowly, and regularly, allowing your stomach and diaphragm to do all the work. Concentrate especially on the exhalation phase. Breathe the air out slowly. And as you exhale, allow your entire body to loosen up and relax. After doing this for a few minutes, you should be feeling pretty tranquil and peaceful. You will have acquired the *mental state of relaxation,* even if your muscles are not yet relaxed.

Now you're ready for the second stage. The goal of the second stage is to loosen up tight muscles and tendons, to make them supple and flexible once again. The way to achieve this is through stretching exercises. You can, for example, roll your head around your shoulders in an arc or circle, stretching it as far as it will go to the right, then forward, then to the left, then backward. If you are especially tense you may not be able to stretch your neck muscles very far. You may have to settle, at first, for a small arc of movement. One woman who tried this technique was so tight that she could not move her head more than a few inches to either side. Not surprisingly, she suffered from headaches, legaches, backaches, and feelings of lassitude and fatigue. The first step in restoring her vitality and energy was to return the flexibility to her muscles.

For the tense person these head rotations should begin gently at first, with an emphasis upon smooth movements instead of fast movements. After stretching the neck muscles, do the same for the feet. Just rotate your feet, one at a time, in an arc. Raise the foot as high as you can, then as far as possible to the left, then downward, then to the right. Repeat this circular movement several times, until the muscles feel loose and relaxed. Try to rotate your toes along with your feet. At first your movements may feel jerky and uncoordinated. But stick with it and after a while you will be able to rotate your feet and head with a smooth, graceful motion. And remember to continue breathing slowly and fully as you stretch your muscles. After stretching your neck and feet muscles, do the same for your eye muscles. Rotate your eyeballs around their sockets in an arc. It's been my experience that if you can stretch and relax the neck and shoulders, feet, and eyeballs, the rest will be easy. From there you can go to the facial muscles, the stomach, the back, the legs, and the arms.

But the key is to use dynamic, stretching movements rather than static, stationary contractions. Some people advocate a different method, I realize. In the Jacobson method, for example, you immediately lie down on the floor and start the relaxation process. You tighten a muscle (say the legs), holding it in one place for a few seconds while you "feel what it's like to be tense," then you let it go. While relaxing it you try to feel what it's like to be relaxed. You alternately tighten and relax each muscle several times, each time trying to reach a deeper level of relaxation than was achieved the last time.

This is a good technique. I highly recommend it. But I do not recommend plunging immediately into it without going through the breathing and stretching phases. Dynamic stretching exercises are among the most neglected exercise techniques in existence. But they are probably the most important for the tense person. If you are very tense and you start contracting your muscles (as Jacobson advocates), you might end up with a "crick" in your neck. The muscles should be gently moved around and stretched before they are contracted. And a mental state of relaxation and peacefulness should be fostered by deep breathing before you actually sit down to relax.

After the deep breathing and stretching sessions, you can choose any technique of relaxation you desire. I've found that one works about as well as another, once you're prepared. Some people prefer to alternately tense and relax. Others like to tell their muscles to "let go." Still others like to imagine scenes from nature, such as peaceful rivers and landscapes. Any of these can work well. But don't feel that you must lie perfectly still. That's where I disagree with some of the relaxation advice I've seen. Sometimes a bit of tension will build up, even during relaxation sessions, and it must be dispelled through motor movements. So feel free to toss and turn a little bit, if you wish.

One final relaxation technique deserves mention: massage. Deep muscle massage is a particularly effective way to promote relaxation and dispel tension. It works best between husband and wives. Then it can be done lovingly and sensuously. When performed in that context massage promotes feelings of well-being and security, as well as relaxation. It makes the participants feel loved, and it gives them an opportunity to demonstrate love in an active way. It draws them closer together. All of these experiences no doubt help to preserve vital energy. And they serve as excellent preludes to marital lovemaking.

STRESS

As mentioned in the introductory chapter, the world's leading authority on stress (and its relationship to vital energy) is Dr. Hans Selye. His research on stress led him to the conclusion that there is only so much vital energy available to each person. When you use up all your vital reserves, you succumb to illness and death. The energy cannot be replenished; it can only be preserved and used wisely.

Selye defines stress as a nonspecific reaction of the body, particularly the nervous system and adrenal glands, to any sort of demand made upon it. According to this definition, stress can be either physical or psychological. It can be due, in other words, to a knife wound or a verbal confrontation. But it's the psychological sources of stress that we're concerned with.

People vary in their reactions to stressful events. What's stressful to one person may not be stressful to another. Take noise, for example. Some people say that they can't concentrate at all while there's any noise around them. Others seem to need a radio, television, or other noisemaker while they study. I'm not one of those people, though. When I have to concentrate I want complete quiet. I can remember staying in the home of an extremely extroverted friend one evening. I was reading a moderately difficult psychology book, and he was writing an article. Before he started, though, he put a tape in his stereo and out blared some popular recording. (He had huge speakers for his tape player—they practically filled up his living room.) The music was so loud that I had to go into my bedroom, close the door, and put pillows along the door cracks in order to read with any amount of efficiency. What was a very stressful situation for me seemed actually invigorating to him.

Despite some exceptions, noise is a source of stress for most people. Studies have shown that exposure to loud noises over a long period of time causes the stomach, blood vessels, and nervous system to put out "stress signals." According to psychiatrists, people who have to work around loud noises are less able to cope with everyday irritations than those whose surroundings are more peaceful. Some have even gone so far as to blame big-city noises—honking horns, blaring radios, loud talking, and strident sirens—for the great number of suicides, murders, fights and child-abuse cases that occur in large cities. The noise doesn't necessarily cause these violent acts. But it lowers the susceptible person's energy and ability to cope with the temptation to react violently.

Stress can result from many sources besides noise. Marital problems frequently cause stress. And the give-and-take of marriage certainly provides much material for the comedian's wit. But divorce is no great solution. In fact, divorce is one of the most stressful events. Your chances of committing suicide or developing a mental illness are greatly increased right after a divorce, especially if you are male. Competition and the race to get ahead are other stressful events. Negative emotions, such as resentment, anger, hatred, and despair, produce stressful reactions.

Stress doesn't necessarily always come from negative events, however. Major life changes, even positive changes, can produce negative reactions. Several years back Dr. Thomas Holmes constructed a "life-events scale" designed to measure the impact of major life changes.[4] He assigned points to each event according to how stressful it was. According to his scale, "death of a spouse" and "divorce" were the two most stressful events, receiving 100 and seventy-three points, respectively. Various other family-related events followed, such as "death of a family member" and "separation." But surprisingly "marriage" received fifty points, suggesting that this positive event is moderately stressful, probably because of the change in life style it produces. "Marital reconciliation" received forty-five points, "retirement" forty-five points, and pregnancy forty points.

This indicates that some life changes, though they are seen positively, are still somewhat stressful. Some psychologists have used this scale to advise people not to initiate too many changes at one time. Dr. Holmes wrote that anytime you approach a score of 300 on his life-events scale, you are headed for trouble. So if you are about to have a child, maybe that's not the time to switch jobs (thirty-six points) or move to a new house (twenty points).

There are some other things that you can do to avoid excessive stress. Dr. Selye advises us to realize that not all stress is bad. In his book *The Stress of Life,*[5] Dr. Selye says that growth and happiness are not fostered "just by staying alive very long." We need some of these life changes in order to grow and to avoid ruts. So all life changes and all stressful events are not necessarily enemies to energy.

This is evidence, however, that people are less able to cope with stresses than they used to be. Dr. Aaron T. Beck, a University of Pennsylvania psychiatrist, points out that "many young people are less able or less willing than before to cope with adversities."[6] What is the reason for this decline in ability to handle stress? The major reason seems to be that we are losing the old supports that gave us our strength and energy. The value system is decaying, religion is losing its effectiveness, families are breaking down, and selfishness is increasing at an alarming rate. But a society must have all of these if it is to remain healthy and energetic. In the last chapter I'll devote some time to these important areas, especially as they relate to energy level.

For now it's important to point out that a strong background of religious faith, family commitments, and a sturdy value system are important weapons in the war against stress. The person who has these in his arsenal can withstand a lot more stress than the person who is without them.

Another of Dr. Selye's ideas for handling stress is to seek diversity, to change your activities and surroundings. Specialization is the style of living and working today. "Our civilization tends to force people into highly specialized occupations which may become monotonously repetitive." He goes on to point out that if we use one part of the mind or body over and over again, that part tends to wear out before the others. The only way that nature can force us out of the groove is through stress.

This is strong evidence in support of a balanced life style—one in which all parts of the body and mind are used. According to this thinking, we should cultivate all the various areas of living (according to our own particular needs and personality styles, of course): social, physical, intellectual, and spiritual. Cultivating a hobby that's completely different from your occupation is also a good idea. Let the person who works primarily with ideas acquire a hobby that requires the use of his hands, such as gardening, woodcarving, carpentry, etc. (Gardening is especially good because it gets us in touch with nature, and with the process of life and growth.) Let the person who works primarily with his hands pursue a hobby that develops his mind. For example, let him read and study to become an expert in some area of his life. These are ways of pursuing the balanced life, of developing all aspects of the mind. And the balanced life is a strong bulwark against stress.

Dr. Selye has one other important piece of advice for handling stress. He thinks we should cultivate the mental set of gratitude. He writes that a sense of gratitude is possibly the best way of assuring security. Gratitude is the opposite of egotism or revengefulness. When we are egotistical we hate it when another prospers. But when we are grateful we actually desire the prosperity of our fellowman; we rejoice in it with him. Our focus, when we are grateful, is upon appreciation and approval rather than upon criticism and dissatisfaction. This message is very close to the message of Christianity. It sounds remarkably similar to what the apostle Paul said when he wrote, ". . . for I have learned, in whatsoever state I am, therewith to be content" (Phil. 4:11); and, "Giving thanks always for all things unto God and the Father in the name of our Lord Jesus Christ" (Eph. 5:20). This is not only a spiritual message; it is advice on how to live the happy and energetic life.

BOREDOM

Surprisingly, boredom can be as stressful and energy-depleting as stress. In fact, boredom is a kind of stress.

One of the best studies on the effects of boredom was done in 1957 by the International Geophysical Year. Scientists were able to interview and observe the reactions of men who had isolated themselves in outposts along the Antarctic. There was not much demanding work to do, and the weather was so cold and windy that outside excursions were impossible. So the men just sat around and watched the equipment. The ensuing boredom had severe effects on them. Many complained that they couldn't concentrate. Although they craved excitement, they also had an increased need for sleep. So the lack of interest and variety produced an even greater energy loss than hard work.

Boredom makes even simple tasks fatiguing. I know that when I was doing my graduate work in psychology I would sometimes get to the point of thinking I couldn't read another word of statistics. My eyes would start to ache and I would get aches in my neck. But then I could switch to another topic that I really liked, and all the aches and pains would disappear. I would read effortlessly and alertly once my interest had been restimulated.

Some psychiatrists have even gone so far as to blame boredom for many crimes of violence. The perpetual troublemaker is often a person who is chronically bored. He can't find satisfaction in the simple pleasures of life. He must seek new and better thrills. Eventually this leads to drug abuse or even murder. Prison psychologists have even used psychological tests to identify the boredom-prone prisoner and try to prevent him from making trouble. They set up a varied, stimulating program of work that requires much physical movement and many shifts of attention.

The solution to boredom, though, is not to keep looking for more and more stimulation, but to enjoy little distractions and simple changes in routine. The person who tries to fight boredom by seeking ever greater sources of stimulation will soon lock himself into a self-defeating pattern. Eventually he will be unable to enjoy the simple pleasures, and he will be unable to work at almost any job. In the end he may take the route of actor George Sanders who ended his own life and left behind a suicide note which read, "I was simply bored."

Anyone who wishes to accomplish anything worthwhile in life must be willing to put up with boredom. Whether it be rearing a child, writing a book, or seeking an education—all involve boredom. You don't handle the boredom by seeking new and better sources of stimulation, but by such little things as varying your routine in subtle ways, finding interest in children, hobbies, eating out, or going to the circus. Boredom is as much a product of the mind as it is of the surroundings. Some people have the ability to take interest in everything. And they are usually the ones that always have abundant energy. I will say more on this subject in the chapter on energy stimulators. For now, it's important to point out that rest will not cure boredom; only interest will. That interest may result from a little more variety or from a mind that can take interest in every little thing, no matter how inconsequential it is to others. It does not result from chronic stimulation-seeking.

FATIGUE

All of the barriers to energy that were discussed above have this one thing in common: they produce the experience of fatigue. Each of them serves as a cause of fatigue.

Other factors are also common causes of fatigue. Overstimulation and overarousal, as well as boredom, can cause energy loss. One study of sixty airline pilots, for example, found an excessive amount of mental fatigue among men in this so-called easy job.[7] About one-fourth of them complained of chronic stomach disorders; another one-fourth had somewhat milder gastric symptoms; many of them experienced sleep disturbance, irritability, and a vague sense of dissatisfaction and restlessness. The problem was that these men were living in a state of overarousal; their working conditions called for too high a level of concentration and too much emotional stimulation.

A similar reaction seems to occur among

people living in a modern city, where they are bombarded daily with more emotional input than they can successfully handle. There is noise, sexual arousal from billboards, movies, television, magazines, and often from the sidewalks and offices; violence (television and otherwise), increasingly stimulating forms of entertainment (especially for teenagers), and even foods so spicy that the natural taste is disguised. All these tend to make people emotionally blunted. They can't enjoy the simpler, more subtle pleasures. Learning new information seems dull, women without the Playboy build are not stimulating, men without Robert Redford's looks are not romantic, life compared to the movies is boring. It's easy to fall into a state of fatigue when the emotions are constantly overstimulated. A fight must practically be waged against the excessive stimulation.

Once a person becomes emotionally, mentally, or physically fatigued, energy is used up at an accelerated rate just to do the same things you used to do without much effort. According to one review on the subject of fatigue, studies have shown that "different individuals use up various amounts of energy doing the same thing, depending upon how they regard the task."[8] Those who are enthusiastic about what they're doing perform almost effortlessly. Those who hate every minute of it use up energy at an alarming rate. The problem is that once you are fatigued, whether it be mental or physical fatigue, you tend to lose your relish for doing even simple tasks. That makes them much harder to do.

Fatigue also makes it more likely that you will make more mistakes and do a poorer job. Several years ago a series of "cockpit studies" were conducted on RAF pilots in England. The pilots were required to "fly" a simulated airplane in laboratory conditions. The reseachers found that as the pilots became more fatigued, they made more errors. This was hardly a surprise. But the most frightening part of it was that as they became more fatigued, they also lowered their standards. They had "an almost irresistible tendency" to relax when the airport was in sight. And as a result they made increasing numbers of mistakes.

You can almost tell how susceptible a person will be to fatigue by looking at the amount of enthusiasm he has about performing some task. Many people begin a task with the attitude that they're not really sure they want to do it. They waver and feel unsure. They are like someone who drives with the brakes on. They lose more energy over fighting with themselves than they do over working at the task itself. There is a lot to say for committing yourself fully to anything you do, nothing held back. As Solomon advises: "Whatsoever thy hand findeth to do, do it with thy might." This is good advice for saving energy. It doesn't mean that you tense up and strain whenever you do something. It simply means that you learn the art of uninhibited effort. You learn to work effortlessly by throwing yourself completely into the task.

I know two women who are polar opposites in their working habits. Both are housewives. One throws herself enthusiastically into every task given her. She teaches a class at her church, does favors, pursues a hobby, exercises, and does all her wifely and maternal chores with the same enthusiasm. She never seems to stop and examine herself to see if she has enough energy or if the task is too difficult. Her basic assumption in life appears to be that she can do anything that's thrown at her, and that she can do it without a lot of effort. As a result, she bubbles over with energy. The other homemaker is different. When anything is asked of her, she spends much time thinking about it, wondering if she has what it takes to complete the task, pondering over the various problems involved in it. And after she's done it, she wastes about as much energy wondering if she did a decent job. As a result, she has far less energy and gets much less done than her friend. There is much to be said for plunging right into a task, doing your best, and then forgetting about it as you take on another task.

There are several other things you can do to combat chronic fatigue. One is to make sure your problem is not physical. All fatigue is not caused from emotional or mental sources, although those seem to be major contributors today. Here are some things that can serve as physical contributors to fatigue:[9]

diabetes
mononucleosis
hepatitis
hypothyroidism

coronary thrombosis
hypoglycemia
anemia
influenza
hemorrhoids
obesity
visual fatigue
menstruation
menopause

Most of these require medical attention. Visual fatigue is a signal that it's time to see an optometrist. Obesity I will cover in a later chapter. And menstruation and menopause simply call for acceptance of the temporary changes that these bring about in energy level and behavior.

In many cases, though, chronic fatigue is caused by a way of thinking and reacting. And the solution to fatigue will differ from one case to the next. One person's energy is being eaten away by an underlying conflict. Perhaps he disliked his late father and now feels guilty over it. The solution is spiritual: love and forgiveness are the keys. Another person has too many demands. Perhaps it is a mother with several young children. She may feel better if she can spend some time by herself occasionally. Perhaps the solution lies in a willing and helpful hand from her husband. Someone else works at a job that requires intense concentration for long periods of time. Short breaks throughout the day and a relaxing hobby in the evenings may help. (Pleasant diversion, rather than rest, usually works best when fatigue is caused by mental factors.) The causes of fatigue vary, and so the optimum solutions vary. But in general, the best barriers against fatigue are an interested and positive mind, a balanced life style, frequent diversions, and a loving, forgiving personality. Against these, fatigue usually makes only temporary inroads.

NOTES

1. Martin Seligman, *Helplessness: On Depression, Development, and Death* (San Francisco: W. H. Freeman, 1975).
2. Frederic Flach, *The Secret Strength of Depression* (Philadelphia: J. B. Lippincott, 1974).
3. Walter C. Alvarez, *Live at Peace with Your Nerves* (New York: Award Books), p. 123.
4. Cited in Linda Pembrook, *How to Beat Fatigue* (New York: Doubleday, 1975).
5. Hans Selye, *The Stress of Life* (New York: McGraw-Hill, 1976).
6. Cited in Pembrook, *How to Beat Fatigue.*
7. *Ibid.*
8. *Ibid.*
9. *Ibid.*

CHAPTER FOUR
FIVE ENERGY STIMULATORS

John Roberts was about as fatigued and listless as a person could possibly be. He was an infantry soldier during World War II. He had been shot three times. He lay in a trench wishing he were dead, like all of his buddies who were spread out around him. John was so weak and dispirited that he wasn't even interested in stopping the bleeding from his wounds. He didn't even have enough energy to raise his head, let alone to pull himself out of the trench that would soon, he thought, be his grave.

And yet ten minutes later, not only had he leaped out of the trench, he had also run several miles at almost full speed. All this took place despite a loss of blood.

What gave him this tremendous upsurge of energy? Where did it come from? A shot of plasma? A dose of vitamins and minerals? A bowl of wheat germ?

No, it was none of these things. What changed

John from a depleted, enervated, dispirited soldier—ready to die rather than move—into an energetic runner was a change in mental outlook. The energy to do these things was there inside him all along. What he needed was the right stimulation to unlock it. That stimulation was provided by one scene, one scene that caused his latent energy to flow. Hearing some rustling noises, John managed to raise his head a few inches to peer down the trench. There, just a few feet away, he saw several rats eating the bodies of the dead soldiers. That one scene brought forth an explosion of energy.

No matter how listless we are, few of us wish to have our energy stimulated in that manner. And the techniques I offer in this chapter are not nearly so drastic. But I think some of them may surprise you because you're used to thinking of them as liabilities instead of energy assets. But each of these can be important energy stimulators. Let's take a look at each in turn.

INTEREST

Your outflow of energy is strongly linked to the amount of interest you have in the world around you. A child at the infant or toddler stage seems abundantly supplied with energy while the middle-aged person appears to have a dry well. While there are obviously physiological differences between these two age groups (in amount of available energy), some of the differences are the result of different interest levels. The toddler is interested in everything around him. He will spend hours going through his mother's pocketbook. Simple things like pots, pans, and spoons fascinate him. He finds it stimulating to put on and take off "Mommy's" or "Daddy's" clothes.

Later, when he is older, his newly developed imagination will serve to maintain his interest in the most commonplace items. A stick of wood becomes a cannon while pebbles assume the shape of soldiers. Prompted by the magic power of his imagination, energy will flow outward in a zest for living.

All too often the mature person feels energy-deprived because he is actually interest-deprived. He feels that he's seen and heard most of the interesting things in his surroundings. Objects, events, and even people that used to interest him now seem commonplace. His imagination, used up in worry and mundane reality, has wasted away. It is no longer used to liven up and motivate. Is it no wonder that his energy level stagnates?

The young child is so interested in and fascinated by what is going on around him that when it comes time for a nap he will fight sleep for all he's worth. His eyes will be almost closing against his will and still he will be struggling to stay awake, fighting separation from all those fascinating people and objects around him. On the other hand, we older folks all too often look forward to bedtime; we wish it would hurry up so that we could be saved from our boredom.

The most common reaction I get to this concept of interest is something like this, "Sure, it's easy for a movie star, scientist, entertainer, or politician to be interested in his work. But how can you maintain your interest in bookkeeping, homemaking, sales work, or such as that?" As Marie Ray writes in her book *How Never to Be Tired*, "It's perfectly true that one job is more interesting than another—*but not nearly so true as that one mind is more interested than another.*"[1]

Even the so-called fascinating jobs usually involve boredom. You'd think that acting is all glamour and interest. But according to the late Leslie Howard, it's all too often a repetitious round of scenes done so many times that they become boring. The same applies to the process of scientific discovery. Read the biographies of any of the great inventors: Thomas Edison, Henry Ford, Marie Curie. What you see repeated over and over again is a boring process of one painstaking experiment after another, made worse by constant failures. What interested these inventors, and what kept them going, was the thought of *the goal* they were pursuing. The work itself was no more interesting than scrubbing out a garbage can.

Think of how many different discoveries were made by people who were willing to take a fresh, interested look at some commonplace object. Women since the beginning of time have complained about the boring demands of child rearing. How could you possibly have a fascinating goal while doing that? And yet the Swiss biologist Jean Piaget created one of the most fascinating theories of intellectual development while simply observing and playing with his own three children. He is now one of the most widely quoted and respected psychologists around. Think also about Sir Isaac Newton and the apple. Or consider Watt and the lid to his kettle.

Several years back my wife was working as a receptionist in a dental laboratory in order to put me through school. I had been to that office many times to visit her. When I first came there, one of the owners showed me around. He explained how each machine worked while I shifted from one foot to the next, thinking about some project I had to complete. I remember my wife telling me several months later about a young medical student who visited the lab. Immediately after the introductions he said, "Now, show me this equipment." He went through the lab looking at the same equipment I had seen (and only vaguely remembered), asking many questions and trying to understand exactly how it worked. It was a rebuke to my lack of interest. There are too many fascinating things all around us to learn about. Every person is an interesting book to peer into. Every object is a fascinating source of knowledge. We should be constantly interested.

So one of the prime contributors to a high energy level is a vital interest in your surroundings and in your work. And one way to accomplish this is simply to look for things to be interested in. People tell me that I have a fascinating job: college teaching. "If I only had a job like yours, I'd always be interested in my work." But the truth is that college teaching gets quite dull, especially after I've taught the same course for about the fifth time. I've found that making subtle changes each time I teach a course—using a different textbook, bringing in material I left out before, finding new questions to ask to stimulate discussion—is one of the best ways to maintain interest in the material. Learning more and more about a topic also makes the material interesting. The more you know about something, the more interesting it becomes. So I try to learn something new about each course I teach. This gives me a new perspective to bring to my students. And, finally, I try to learn something about my students. I try to take an interest in them. For people are the most interesting subjects.

I've found that other people use similar techniques to make their work more interesting. One homemaker said the following, "I hate to wash dishes. To me that's the dullest, most unsatisfying work possible. There's no way to make it interesting. But I've noticed that when I have another woman over and she helps me wash dishes, our conversation makes the dishwashing seem easy and even fun. Sometimes it is over too soon."

The person who could invent a way to make all work interesting would no doubt become the richest man in the world. But the solution doesn't always lie in enlivening the work. All too often a balance has to be reached between finding something you're interested in and being interested in what you're already doing. As clinical psychologist Zygmunt Piotrowski points out, strong, spontaneous, lasting interest can be an excellent substitute for consciously planned activities. The problem with relying too heavily upon interest alone is that it might make us hesitate to tackle difficulties and obstacles. The strong-willed, disciplined person who forces himself to do something whether he likes it or not will be less thwarted by obstacles than the person who follows his own interests. But the person who is impelled by his own spontaneous interests may gain a deeper satisfaction from his work and use up less energy doing it than the driven person.

Somehow we need to achieve a balance between doing what interests us and trying to be interested in what we're doing. I've seen children, young boys, who didn't seem able to learn anything in school. And yet they could memorize massive and detailed facts about the lives of baseball players. That is a powerful testimony for the importance of interest. We should select a life work that interests us. We should do some things every day that we're interested in. But we should also realize that part of the solution is to find new ways to be interested in things we think are boring. The key in both cases is interest. If we are vitally interested in what we're doing, we'll rarely have problems with energy level.

OPTIMISM

Another important attitude is that of optimism. Some people are just naturally more optimistic than others. As I mentioned earlier, extroverts are by nature more optimistic than introverts. To a large extent your general level of optimism or pessimism is strongly influenced by your genes.

But I'm not talking about your general level of optimism. I'm talking about the optimism or confidence with which you approach a task. Some people seem to function under the assumption that they will be successful at whatever they do. They begin tasks easily and rarely procrastinate (sometimes they hop just as easily to another task before completing the first, but that's a different story). Other people begin every task, no matter how competent they are at it, with the assumption that they will run into serious problems, that they will run out of energy, or that someone will come along and tell them to stop.

Now, I'm not knocking a healthy amount of insecurity or pessimism. As I point out in the next section, these attitudes have their place, especially if they lead to better planning and greater effort. But you have to have a certain amount of optimism and confidence in your ability to complete a task without having to drain yourself of vital energy in the process.

Of course, one way to achieve this optimistic mental set is to choose work that you feel comfortable with. Decide, for example, whether you are "task-oriented" or "person-oriented." The task-oriented person likes to work without having to worry about getting along with others. The person-oriented type, on the other hand, likes to be around people. He is usually stimulated by external forces, while the task-oriented person is motivated internally. If you are a task-oriented person, you might try to take on work that mainly involves things. If you are person-oriented, you will probably need others around to stimulate you.

But don't be too upset if you fret over every demand that's placed on you, dread being evaluated, and fear that what you've already done wasn't good enough. Don't be upset, in other words, if you're an insecure person. For insecurity is a great source of motivation. Let's take an in-depth look at it in the next section.

INSECURITY

Insecurity always implies some sort of uncertainty. The insecurity can come from inside (a lack of confidence) or it can spring from the environment or situation (such as when men go to battle; their lives are uncertain, insecure). Under normal circumstances, however, there are many types of insecurity. A few of the more common are listed below.

Common Manifestations of Insecurity.

1. Social insecurity. This is a common form of insecurity. People who are socially insecure are uncertain as to whether other people will accept or reject them, like or dislike them. Most of us are more or less uncertain over the reactions of others, but we handle our insecurity in different ways. Some people seek positions of power that allow them to control other people. Others reject

people before they can be rejected; some run from person to person, seeking approval. Asking for unnecessary advice or help, kidding or teasing, and trying to get attention may all represent ways of handling social insecurity.

2. Financial insecurity. Some people live in fear of losing their jobs. This seems to be fairly common today, with the job situation undergoing such frequent fluctuations and fewer jobs available than people who desire them.

3. Status insecurity. This occurs when people are insecure over their family backgrounds or their positions in life. It is a common motivator behind upward social striving.

4. Meeting standards. Many people are insecure over their ability to live up to rigidly unrealistic standards. They desire perfect performance. Perfection is not humanly possible; so insecurity results.

Causes of Insecurity. One cause of insecurity is high emotionality. Persons with high emotional drives often fear that they will lose control of themselves. Their churning, bubbling emotions—lurking just below the surface—threaten to get the better of them. Often they unconsciously fear that their emotional energy may be released in the form of hatred, aggression, assertiveness, or possibly even sexual behavior. As a result they can never come to feel secure and at ease in social situations.

Another source of insecurity is the tendency of a person to compare himself with absolute standards. Many times insecure people think in the following manner: If I do not have total calmness, then I am totally upset. If I am not a total success, then I am a total failure. If I do not possess total knowledge, then I am totally ignorant. The person with a tendency to think in terms of absolutes is almost always insecure because absolutes can never be achieved; they are humanly impossible. Of all causes of insecurity, this is one of the most frequent. It breeds a chronic fear of failure.

Bob Drake was an amateur boxer I knew who had a pathological fear of losing a match. He was an excellent boxer; but because of his desire for total success, he avoided as many non-tournament boxing matches as possible. He feared defeat too much. As a result of his tendency to avoid all but the championship matches, he did not polish his skills to the fine edge he needed in order to win. His fear of failure, of losing a match, caused him to be less of a fighter than he might have been.

Another cause of insecurity is the failure to develop proper coping skills. We all have areas of insecurity. Some are insecure about speaking, others about working, some about driving, some about flying. But some people have a general lack of ability to cope with all but a few situations. Often these people were overly restricted as children. Their parents very quickly squelched any attempts at self-assertion and self-reliance to the point that the child came to rely too heavily upon others.

Finally, insecurity can result from a desire never to be wrong, never to make a mistake. The person who dreads making a mistake must protect at all costs his feelings of omnipotence; and the best protection is not acting at all. Thus such people rarely do anything.

Adaptive Features of Insecurity. Insecurity has great potential as a motivating force, a source of energy. People who accomplish a great deal in life are often insecure types who feel compelled to work hard in order to alleviate their insecurity. This is insecurity in the adaptive sense. A person insecure because of a lack of knowledge sets out to learn as much as possible. The person insecure over being beaten up by the neighborhood bully takes self-defense lessons. The person insecure over his status or position in the world works that much harder to acquire a better status and a better position. And the person insecure over his job situation does everything in his power to improve his skills and qualifications so that if he does lose his job he will easily find another one; or he works that much harder on his present job in order to become invaluable to his employers.

I know one man—a fairly well-known writer—who was to appear on a talk show that specializes in "confrontation." The producers were going to invite to the show several people who were hostile to my author friend's position. This made him feel quite insecure and anxious about his appearance on the show. But he handled the insecurity in an adaptive manner— he read up on his subject and called other experts so that he would be thoroughly prepared. As a result, he did very well.

The fact that insecurity—uncertainty—is a great energizing force is no new concept. Developmental psychologist Daniel Berlyne theorized that childhood curiosity about the world is the result of an underlying insecurity, a lack of knowledge which propels children to learn as much as they can. They realize that in comparison with adults they are deficient in knowledge. So they ask questions and observe; they acquire a massive amount of information in the few years from birth to early childhood. Once speech is developed, children will typically ask thousands of questions: who, what, why, where, when, and how. They attempt to reduce their insecurity (temporarily) by setting off on the most intense knowledge-seeking excursion that they will ever experience in any period in their lives.

This is as it should be. Insecurity should always lead to action in order to reduce the insecurity. It's a shame that as adults we acquire inhibitions against asking questions, against seeking knowledge in an unabashed, uninhibited manner.

Of course, insecurity only serves as a motivator to action; it does not determine the course of action. Insecurity can lead to the establishment of brutal dictatorships, as it did in the case of Adolph Hitler and others formed from the same mold. On the other hand, insecurity can lead to well-organized forms of political and legal systems, to new knowledge, or to well-prepared minds.

People who experience strong feelings of insecurity usually also have a well-developed sense of inferiority. In fact, feelings of inferiority are one specific manifestation of insecurity. Both often spring from a similar process: comparing ourselves unfavorably with a standard. In the case of insecurity, the comparison is made with an absolute standard—the desire for perfection in some area. With feelings of inferiority, on the other hand, we compare ourselves unfavorably with other people.

In a sense inferiority feelings are simply realistic experiences. Practically every single person on the earth is superior to us in some way, and vice versa. If we compare ourselves with another human being in an area in which he is strong and we are weak, we will almost surely feel inferior.

However, strong inferiority feelings are not simply realistic assessments. They are pervasive feelings of worthlessness and lack. The person with strong feelings of inferiority believes that he doesn't measure up to other people. But rather than handling these feelings by identifying and developing his own assets, he usually spends much of his time envying those of others. He becomes a spectator.

Causes of Inferiority Feelings. What could cause a person to experience habitual, pervasive feelings of inferiority? The possibilities are infinite but the following have frequently been associated with a persistent sense of inferiority:

1. *Physical deficits.* Under this heading the most common would be physical unattractiveness. We place quite a priority in this society upon physical attractiveness in both men and women. The unattractive person has one strong strike against him to begin with; he comes up short in an area that society values.

Other physical deficits are also frequently associated with feelings of inferiority. Short people, for example, are often made to feel inferior. The emphasis in this culture is generally that bigger is better. The small person is at a disadvantage when this yardstick is applied.

2. *Late maturity.* Research has consistently found that boys who reach puberty at later ages (around fourteen or fifteen) have stronger feelings of inferiority and worthlessness than those who reach puberty early (around twelve or thirteen). It makes sense. The physically retarded male is hurt in areas that are considered to be important indicators of self-worth: athletics and heterosexual relations. Unless the late-bloomer can compensate in some other area, he's at a tremendous disadvantage. This research has followed early and late maturers into adulthood and found that the advantages gained by reaching puberty early are not lost until the late thirties and early forties.

3. *An overpowerful parent.* Parents who are exceptionally attractive, knowledgeable, powerful, or famous may often provoke feelings of

inferiority in their children. People who compare themselves unfavorably with others may be practicing a habit they learned in childhood, when they felt small and inadequate next to a powerful parent.

4. *Critical parents.* If one or both parents are highly critical, their child is likely to grow up with the feeling that he doesn't measure up. This feeling is likely to be aggravated if the parents themselves meet the criteria listed in 3.

5. *An idealized sibling.* An exceptionally attractive, powerful, high-achieving brother or sister may also cause unfavorable comparisons to be made. The situation is aggravated if the parents themselves make the unfavorable comparison. One young man I knew acquired a strong inferiority complex because his parents constantly doted upon his more attractive older brother.

Adaptive Features of Inferiority Feelings. A sense of inferiority could not possibly be a very harmful attribute. Too many people experience it (probably the majority of people, at least at some time in their lives). If happiness were restricted only to those who possess unbounded self-satisfaction and self-assurance, then few would ever be contented. If only very self-assured people achieved anything in life, then little would be accomplished. In actuality, inferiority feelings are among the greatest energizers of effort and accomplishment. They are, I believe, at least as important as talent, and may often efficiently substitute for it. As Edward Strecker and Kenneth Appel write in their book *Discovering Ourselves:* "The inferiority complex has been called the 'golden complex,' and a book has been written on the *Glory of the Imperfect*. As a matter of fact, it would be a sorry world without this sense of the imperfect, without this knowledge of our limitations. As Browning says, it is the 'Spark that disturbs our clod.' It keeps us striving to reach beyond our poor selves. It prevents us from reclining in smug satisfaction with what we have and what we are. It is the very breath of inspiration and progress."[2]

The sense of inferiority instills a fighting spirit within us. Why should the superior person strive to develop his assets? He already has a strong sense of his own self-worth. Excessive effort is unnecessary. Only those who feel the sting of inferiority will make a strong effort to cultivate their strengths.

Whether we're talking about insecurity, inferiority, or both (which is most usually the case), these "complexes" provide fuel for the fight of life. But the gold mine of energy they give us can remain untapped. The person whose past history repeated the lesson to him, "You are inferior. You don't measure up," may simply submit to those feelings. His attitude may become, "You are right. What is the use of struggling?" rather than, "I must prove you wrong. I must prove my own worth."

In order to make maximum use of these dynamic forces the following advice should prove helpful.

Managing Insecurity and Inferiority.

1. Don't compare yourself with others. This is old advice, but it's useful. No two individuals are alike. One person's strength is another's weakness. Even when two people have the same talents, they will still use those talents in their own individual manner. How can Shakespeare be compared with Charles Dickens? Each achieved the height of literary creativity, and yet their styles were completely different. You cheat yourself when you compare your own strengths with those of others. You fail to learn to appreciate your own individuality.

Of course, this presupposes that you have identified your areas of strength and are currently developing those strengths. Unfortunately this is not the case with many people. Too many people have not bothered to take extensive looks at their own personalities with the intent of developing their potential. This neglect leads to stagnation. Those who don't develop their own strengths usually are left to envy those who have developed theirs.

2. Admit your human nature, your fallibility. This is one of the most common sources of chronic insecurity: the person comes to evaluate himself in terms of absolute standards. As Maxwell Maltz observes, our insecurity is usually not caused by a lack of resources, "but due to the fact that we use a false measuring stick. We compare our actual abilities to an imagined 'ideal,' perfect, or absolute self. Thinking of yourself in terms of absolutes induces insecurity."[3] He goes on to point out that the insecure person

thinks that he should be "good"—period; or that he should be competent—period. These are goals to aim for but never quite reach. Stop thinking in terms of absolutes.

3. Make use of overcompensation. Probably the best way to handle feelings of insecurity (or inferiority) is to concentrate your energy upon one goal or one asset and pursue it with a sense of dedication. Psychologists and educators might scoff at this advice, calling it too narrow. But it is so common in the histories of famous people that it would appear to be almost *the* sole route to recognition.

There appear to be two types of overcompensation. In the first type, you focus upon something that you lack, but strongly desire. This is the Charles Atlas type of overcompensation: a ninety-eight-pound weakling devotes himself to a lifetime of weightlifting until he finally wins the Mr. America bodybuilding contest. Other examples of this type of overcompensation abound. Theodore Roosevelt was weak and sickly as a boy. Paderewski had weak, delicate fingers. Dr. Trudeau, himself afflicted with tuberculosis, established one of the world's most famous fresh-air sanitoriums.

With the second type of overcompensation, you take some specific strength that you already possess and develop it to its maximum. Some strengths have obvious potential. Writing skill, athletic ability, business acumen, a pleasing personality are all easily identified strengths and should be developed. But other strengths are dormant; they aren't easily identified until some enterprising person makes use of them. Clifford W. Beers presents an example of a person who overcompensated in this latter sense of the word. He had been insane, committed to an asylum. After his release he wrote a book that has become a classic in its area: *A Mind That Found Itself*. In it he documented his experiences and offered encouragement to those similarly afflicted. Then he went a step further and founded the National Committee for Mental Hygiene. This is an excellent example of energy well used—the energy itself springing from an inferiority-breeding affliction.

WORRY

Worry seems like an odd habit to put in a chapter on "Energy Stimulators." Worry, we've all been taught to understand, is one of the prime sources of energy waste. This is true. But worry is also a hidden energy stimulator. Anyone who worries should realize that there is an almost electrical energy that goes into worry sessions. That energy is the raw product for creative thinking, imagination, and problem-solving, if it is properly used. The key is not to stop worrying, but to learn how to use "worry energy" in a positive, constructive manner.

Worry is defined in the American Heritage Dictionary as "mental uneasiness or anxiety." This uneasiness is unrelated to anything in the immediate present. It has to do with a future event that the worrier believes, or fears, may come about.

The key element in understanding worry is imagination. Worriers have vivid imaginations. This is both their strength and their weakness, depending upon how it is developed and used.

Imagination. Imagination is the key to any kind of human motivation. Little could be accomplished without it. Even the capacity for self-improvement springs from the imagination. Dugald Stewart says about worry that, "It prevents us from ever being completely satisfied with our present condition and with our past attainments and engages us continually in the pursuit of some untried enjoyment or of some ideal excellence."[4]

Consider other statements about the importance of imagination. "Imagination is more important than knowledge" (Albert Einstein). "Hold a picture of yourself long and steadily enough in your mind's eye and you will be drawn toward it. Picture yourself vividly as defeated and that alone will make victory impossible. Picture yourself vividly as winning and that alone will contribute immeasurably to success. Great living starts with a picture, held in your imagination, of what you would like to do or be" (Harry Emerson Fosdick). "You must have a clear mental picture of the correct thing before you can do it successfully" (Alex Morrison).

So imagination is the key to accomplishing anything in life; it is the prime motivator behind human action, more so than will power. It is the major source of mental energy. The French psychologist Emile Coue postulated that, "When the Will tries to overcome the Imagination, the

141

Imagination overcomes the Will." In other words, mental pictures that we habitually hold in our minds serve as goals toward which we automatically strive.

Worriers are people who are making use of this gift of imagination. But they are using it in a nonproductive way. The nonproductive worrier holds a negative image in his mind. And his mind naturally struggles to make that image a reality.

But the fact that worriers have such vivid imaginations means they have a great potential for growth. This same imagination which works so vividly to their disadvantage in a state of nonproductive worry will work just as well to their advantage in a state of problem-solving activity. This is why Maxwell Maltz, in one of his best-selling books, advises the worrier to set aside time during which he actively, systematically uses his imagination in order to implement his own growth.

Dr. Maltz also paints a way in which worry can be put to positive and constructive use. Usually when we worry we set up a condition that might happen and then we imagine in our minds the thing actually happening. We experience in our imagination all the pain, passivity, and anxiety that we would experience if the event really came to pass. We usually use every resource of our imagination to make the painful event as detailed and realistic as possible. As Maltz points out, we can use the exact same process that we use in negative worry to build up our self-concept or our feeling that success is imminent. So he advises the chronic worrier to use his imagination to play with the idea of success. The worrier is used to thinking about failure. But Dr. Maltz thinks he should now do exactly what he does when he worries, but this time he should think of success rather than failure, a desirable outcome instead of a feared outcome. This is worrying in reverse.

Here is excellent advice for the worrier. Here is constructive and channeled worry. Don't stop worrying; to take that advice would simply mean to stop using your imagination. Rather, change the content of your worrying. Instead of worrying about an undesirable outcome, begin to worry about the possibility of something positive. Start off by saying, "Now just suppose I could bring this about." Then start saying, "How would I bring this about?" From there you go to the idea, "Well, it is possible to do this." And eventually, after adding fine details and vivid mental pictures, you come to the point of actually saying to yourself, "Now, what can I do to bring this about?" This is productive worry; this is worry that lends itself to growth. And this is worry that encourages a high level of energy output rather than the kind that depletes energy.

Another form of constructive worry is problem-solving. Worriers need to have their intellects actively engaged most of the time. Otherwise they tend to direct their attention to something unproductive. Research has demonstrated that worriers possess a better ability to generate vivid fantasies than non-worriers. Unless this ability is directed toward identifying and finding solutions to problems it will be used up in apprehensive brooding. Whenever the worrier finds himself passively brooding over something he fears will happen, he should say something like the following to himself: "What's happening to me now is that energy is flooding my mind and activating my imagination. That energy is the raw product of creativity. But I am using it in an unproductive and negative fashion. In fact, I'm turning it against my own body, wearing out my organs and disturbing my body chemistry. I should be using this energy to solve a problem of some sort." Then he should act upon those thoughts.

To a large extent the chronic worrier is not responsible for the fact that energy continuously bombards and fuels his imagination. The chances are good that he is a highly emotional person by nature, and that emotionality is what's really activating his mind. He's not responsible for the fact that he has an energetic mind, but he is reponsible for the use he puts that energy to. Like it or not, all worriers are potential "idea men." They are creators, artists, problem-solvers. The way for them to handle their worry tendencies is to turn that energy into ideas, solutions, inventions, and innovations.

Maladaptive Features of Nonproductive Worry. Maladaptive worry—worry that's not directed toward a solution to some problem or does not involve creating a positive enjoyable image of ourselves in action—has many obvious maladaptive features. In the first place, worry tends to sap our energy and produce a state of fatigue. The chronic worrier depletes his vital resources and his energy; he thus is unable to use them in productive work or recreation.

Appetite may diminish in the chronic worrier. Worriers often are too thin. Perhaps a normal weight level could be reached if the person would learn to worry adaptively; food would taste better and the digestive system would work more efficiently.

Nonproductive worry also leads to sleep problems. Not only does the nonproductive worrier tend to establish negative mental habits—once he gets into bed, a time in which worry of all forms ought to be relinquished, he interrupts his sleep and relaxation by thinking the same thoughts he's been thinking all day. Pretty soon the bed may come to be associated, not with restfulness and relaxation, but with worry and concern.

Many psychosomatic disorders are also the result of worry. Tooth decay, ulcers, headaches, backaches, neckaches, digestive problems, even diseases such as asthma and cancer can be caused by nonproductive worry.

One of the worst features about nonproductive worry is the state of helplessness and passivity that the worrier tends to experience. If the worry session is not devoted to finding solutions to a problem or to creating positive mental images—if it is simply devoted to anxious experience of pain that *may* come because of some real or imagined event in the future—then the person is simply producing in his own eyes a self-image of helplessness and passivity. He is telling himself that nothing can be done about the problem. He is establishing a habit of not dealing actively with problems.

The Constructive Worrier. The solution for people who worry nonproductively does not lie in their heeding the usual advice: "Don't worry." Not to worry would require that these people give up one of their greatest resources: rich imagination. It would require them to turn back the flood of mental energy—an impossible task. The best solution over the long term is not to stop worrying but to become a more constructive worrier, a better brooder. The worrier needs to change the content of what he worries about; he does not need to cease "worrying."

Imagination is the raw product of creativity and problem-solving ability. Without imagination we could not solve advanced problems; with imagination we have the potential for highly creative endeavors. Among worriers, the raw products of creativity—imagination, abstract thinking, mental alertness—have been well put to use; they are highly developed. The only problem is that they have been put to the wrong use. So my advice to worriers (and the advice that I have taken) is *don't stop worrying;* just change the content of your thoughts when you worry. Don't brood about how people have mistreated you or what bad thing may come upon you or your loved ones (unless by so brooding you can more efficiently grapple with that bad thing); this is negative, unproductive brooding. Instead, focus upon solutions to problems, creative endeavors, self-concept-enhancing exercises.

The pages of books listing outstanding achievements and achievers are replete with the names of individuals who successfully utilized their tendency to brood and worry (i.e., their imagination). Isaac Asimov stands out as a highly successful chronic worrier. Asimov has been called "The Human Writing Machine." He has written two hundred books and over a thousand magazine and newspaper articles. It's estimated that he writes about twelve books and forty magazine articles every year in addition to the numerous speeches and lectures that he gives. His typical day begins at 8:00 A.M., at which time he sits down at his typewriter and types steadily at the rate of ninety words per minute until approximately ten o'clock at night.

What keeps him going at such a high pace? A *Reader's Digest* article on Isaac Asimov's career revealed that he writes prolifically in order to stave off a tendency to worry and fret. Asimov, when he's not writing, worries that his plane will crash, that his wife has been hurt in an automobile accident, about losing his money, about becoming rich. But obviously here is a man who is adaptively adjusting to his tendency to worry in two ways: Number one, by distracting himself with work; and number two, by utilizing his imagination in a creative fashion.

Sometimes, however, it's not worry in general that we have to deal with but specific worries. Something may have come up that seems to demand our attention; and our attention takes the form of worry. In order to adaptively cope with specific worry, Dale Carnegie[5] has made the following suggestions:

First, ask yourself, "What is the worst that could possibly happen?" List the very worst possible outcomes. Next, prepare to accept the worst things that you have written down. And, finally, calmly proceed to improve upon the worst, to find some ways in which you can salvage the situation.

Write down specifically what it is you are worried about. Often our worries are vague, diffused sorts of images; and we don't know exactly what it is we are upset over.

Get busy doing something. Start performing some useful work or activity. This is one of the best ways of distracting our attention from what we're worried about. Studies have shown that combat veterans who had been shot and were bleeding from painful wounds forgot their pain for many hours when actively engaged in some activity which required all of their attention. Once the activity was over, the pain all of a sudden became unbearable. The same thing applies to psychological pain. We can forget something, no matter how painful it is, when our attention is actively focused upon something else.

Forget trivialities. Remember that, "Life is too short to be little." Distract your attention from little things that people have done or said.

Ask yourself, "What are the chances of this happening?" Worries over such things as health, car accidents, airplane crashes, etc., may vanish when we sit down with the statistics and look at the percentage of people who experience them. Often we find that our chances of this ever happening are so slim that the statistic in itself will be reason enough to stop worrying about it.

Cooperate with the inevitable. When things are going to happen and there's nothing we can do about them, be like the palm tree that bends with the wind but never snaps. Just as sometimes it's necessary to give in to a depression and experience it actively, aggressively, and with no apologies, so it also is necessary to allow disaster to happen to us, to let it break around us like waves against the rocks.

And above all, keep in mind that worry is a form of energy. Like electricity, it can serve you well if you harness it. But it can slowly murder you if you don't.

NOTES

1. Marie Ray, *How Never to Be Tired* (Indianapolis, Ind.: Bobbs-Merrill, 1938).
2. Edward Strecker and Kenneth Appel, *Discovering Ourselves* (New York: Macmillan, 1958).
3. Maxwell Maltz, *Psycho-Cybernetics: The New Way to a Successful Life* (Englewood Cliffs, N.J.: Prentice-Hall, 1960).
4. Cited in Mack R. Douglas, *How to Make a Habit of Succeeding* (Kentwood, Mi: Zondervan).
5. Dale Carnegie, *How to Stop Worrying and Start Living* (New York: Simon & Schuster, 1948).

CHAPTER FIVE
SIX STEPS TO QUICK ENERGY WHEN YOU NEED IT

We all have times when we crave a quick energy boost. Sometimes the need for an energy lift is created by a difficult task we are about to undertake—one we're afraid we won't be able to handle. Other times our need comes from a feeling of fatigue or lack of motivation during some task we're already working at. This chapter is written with those times in mind. These six suggestions should help you call up plenty of energy when you need it right away.

BREATHE DEEPLY AND FULLY

Breathing is one of the main contributors to energy level. How a person breathes determines both his immediate level of energy (his feelings of vigor and vitality) and the efficiency with which he uses his supply of long-term vital energy.

Breathing seems like such a commonplace and

simple process that you'd hardly think it worth dwelling upon in a book on energy. Many people get the idea that there is some "key" or "pill" that will automatically provide them with an abundant flow of energy. And people who write books on energy tend to cater to that desire, often providing recipes for "energy milkshakes" and other such magical formulas. But the answer to energy problems lies in attention to little, neglected mental and physical functions, such as breathing. Unless you breathe correctly, even massive doses of vitamins, minerals, organic fruits, and all the other nostrums won't give you the energy you desire.

Modern life is incompatible with correct breathing. The chances are good that if you work at a desk, read a lot, or do sedentary work you probably breathe poorly. Unless you take strong precautions to counter it, you will just naturally slip into the habit of breathing shallowly, and thereby inviting fatigue, lethargy, boredom, and even depression.

The person who works at a desk will tend to slump. This compresses his lungs, interferes with his diaphragm, and prevents full breaths from being taken. The person who is sedentary much of the day doesn't feel the need to breathe fully and deeply because he doesn't exert himself. Even if he goes home and exercises he will still have lost much vital energy during the day, and his brain will have been deprived of much vital oxygen that it needs to function sharply and alertly. Some studies suggest that deep breathing improves our memories by as much as 7 percent.

I can remember the first time I recharged my energy level by putting this advice into action. I was standing in line at registration for college classes. Standing in line always made me feel tired, listless, and even depressed. But I never could figure out why. After all, standing up, even for as much as two or three hours, doesn't use up *that* much energy. But one day, in a burst of insight, I concluded that the reason I felt so listless was that while standing in line for so long I gradually began to breathe more and more shallowly. So I tried a little experiment. I stood up straight (I begin to slump as I start to feel listless—another energy drain) and started breathing full, deep breaths, using my stomach and diaphragm muscles instead of my throat and chest. It worked like a charm. Both my spirits and my energy level remained high the whole time I stood in line. And after registration was over I still felt good enough to go right home and study (usually I felt like doing nothing).

It's amazing to see what a simple thing like deep breathing can do for you. It helps you overcome boredom and listlessness. It gives you a feeling of self-mastery and vitality. It clears out the cobwebs and helps you think more efficiently.

I've even found that I can instill a sense of determination and purpose in myself simply by breathing with determination. Breathing is the smallest common denominator of life. Whatever attitude you undertake along with this function will quickly spread to all your other attitudes. If you breathe hesitantly, passively, and weakly you will feel hesitant, passive, and weak. But even your courage can be increased by purposeful determined breathing. Just try it! The next time you feel bored, afraid, listless, unmotivated, fatigued, or helpless, just start breathing with purpose and determination. At first don't even think about the thing you fear, or your feelings of fatigue, or the obstacles in your way. Just think about breathing purposefully. Do it for several minutes. Then, when the attitude of determination follows your breathing (as it always does, sooner or later), transfer that attitude to your specific energy problem.

You can even use breathing to help you overcome procrastination. If there's a task you've been avoiding, don't try to force yourself to tackle it by an effort of will. Just start breathing deeply and purposefully. Pretty soon you'll experience the *attitude* of determination and purpose. When that occurs, you'll be ready to tackle that dreaded task.

The key to correct breathing is to use the stomach and diaphragm, not the mouth, nose, throat, or chest. Sit up straight and imagine that you're breathing only with the top part of your stomach, just beneath your ribs. One precaution: be careful about overbreathing. You can alter the oxygen/carbon dioxide ratio by breathing too deeply for too long a period of time. This can cause hyperventilation. It's a good idea to breathe deeply for three or four breaths, then moderately for three or four breaths, if you have a tendency to hyperventilate.

MAINTAIN GOOD POSTURE

Good posture goes hand-in-hand with full, deep breathing. In fact, proper breathing techniques are not likely to be very effective unless accompanied by erect posture. When you slump forward, as people who work at a desk inevitably do, your rib cage is thrust downward on top of your stomach and diaphragm. Not only does this compress your lungs, thereby encouraging shallow breathing; it also prevents your diaphragm and stomach muscles from doing their job. Since they can no longer control breathing, the burden falls upon your throat. But throat breathing, over the years, can cause problems. It impairs the full, rich quality of your voice, raising its pitch and even giving it a raspy quality. And it throws a strain upon the throat muscles, often causing them to wear out before their time.

But the damage due to poor posture goes beyond throat weakness and improper breathing. Many important organs are compressed and prevented from doing their job when you slump. The thymus gland, the lungs, the heart, the stomach, and many others are squeezed so that they can't function properly. Several years of this will bring on disease and premature aging. Your organs need to do their job in a free, uncramped atmosphere. That atmosphere is provided when you maintain good posture.

Poor posture is the sign of defeat, dejection, and weakness. You can be sure that the young woman who slumps forward until her stomach bulges out is too weak to have abundant energy. You can assume that the young man who allows his neck to curve inward and his shoulders to droop forward is too dispirited to work effectively and persistently. If he's not dejected now, he soon will be as a result of poor posture. If you were a personnel manager looking for energetic young people to hire, you wouldn't want those two. You'd be looking for people who sit up straight in their chairs. For if they don't have the energy even to sit and stand correctly, how could they have the energy to work productively?

Here is one of the great psychological principles upon which our moods, attitudes, and mental states are formed. This was first pointed out by William James, the father of American psychology. It goes like this: Your posture will reflect your mental state. We all know this. If you're depressed, tired, or bored, you'll tend to slump. But the really profound part of this is that *your posture will in turn determine your mental state*. If you assume the posture of the defeated, the dejected, and the weak, you will soon come to feel defeated, dejected, and weak. It's inevitable.

But the good news is that if you assume the posture of energy, determination, and cheerfulness you will soon come to feel energetic, determined, and cheerful. This is also inevitable.

Your mind attempts to be consistent with your body. So if you wish to be a disciplined, energetic person you must first assume the posture (and breathing) of a disciplined energetic person. Sit up straight and erect, with your shoulders back, head up, and stomach in. This is military posture, I realize. But the goal of the military is to promote discipline. And the first step toward that goal is disciplined posture. Not only do you give other people the image of an energetic, disciplined person when you sit or stand erect, you also give your own unconscious mind that image. It then tries to help foster those traits of energy and discipline by making you feel like the sort of person who has them.

So the first step toward becoming an energetic, "together" person is to assume the posture of an energetic, "together" person. I realize that this is not as easy and as quick as an "energy milkshake" or vitamin pills. But it is the result of the wisdom of the ages. And it works! Just try it the next time you feel fatigued, depressed, bored, or listless. Or try it when you are about to undertake a difficult task.

One precaution: Don't make the mistake of trying to hold yourself rigidly in one position for any length of time. That's not what good posture is all about. Good posture is much more flexible and dynamic than that. Any posture becomes quickly fatiguing if it's held rigidly—even good posture. Sit or stand up straight, but move about a bit. Make sure that each muscle is allowed to stretch and move. You might even want to allow your muscles to droop forward every now and then. But always return to an erect posture. And make your posture graceful and flexible, not rigid and stiff. Finally, those of us who do a lot of desk work, or any work that requires bending forward, need to take intermittent posture-and-deep-breathing breaks. Just sit up erect and take several deep breaths. This practice will pay dividends in alertness, health, and mental attitude.

INSPIRATION SESSIONS

Many of our energy problems are caused by poor habits of thinking. Sometimes we lose sight of our goals, or those goals fail to stimulate and motivate us. Sometimes our courage falters. Sometimes resentments, guilt, despair, and other negative thinking patterns eat up our energy and make us feel tired and helpless.

What we need, when this happens, is a burst of inspiration—the sort of inspiration that disinhibits energy, elevates our thinking, enhances our confidence and faith, and makes us feel alive and invigorated.

One way to inspire yourself in this manner is to read inspirational literature. Several good books are available: *The Power of Positive Thinking* by Norman Vincent Peale, *Psycho-Cybernetics* by Maxwell Maltz, *Be Glad You're Neurotic!* by Louis Bisch, and *I Love the Word Impossible* by Ann Kiemel, among others. Each of these books has the power to change a negative mental state into a positive one in just a matter of minutes. Each can encourage an outburst of energy, confidence, and motivation.

I would strongly recommend that you start off the day by reading a few pages from one of these books. I've found that a short morning session spent with an inspirational book will encourage a high level of energy and a mental state of optimism and courage that will last the entire day. It's particularly important to have an inspiration session right before you undertake a particularly difficult task. It will call forth your greatest efforts and your deepest levels of energy. Resources that you never knew you had will be tapped. This method has been used by people who dread public speaking, to infuse themselves with confidence and determination. It's been used by people who are trying to fight chronic procrastination. One man used it to help himself get through a difficult college course. Whenever he felt his determination slip and his discipline fade, he would simply pull out an inspirational book, and use it to get a fresh breath of energy and life. It's been used to successfully fight depression, fatigue, listlessness, despair, defeat, worry, and a host of other negative mental states.

These inspiration sessions, in order to be effective, should take place at frequent intervals. A one-shot approach won't work. Inspiration, like conversion, requires constant attention and frequent application. As Billy Sunday replied, when criticized that his "quick conversions" didn't last long, "neither does a bath."

Of course, by far the best inspirational book available is the Bible. There is a power available in the Word of God that automatically chases away depression, fear, despair, and dejection. God's Word automatically infuses us with new energy, purpose, faith, and dedication. As Christ said to his disciples, "The words that I speak unto you, they are spirit, and they are life" (John 6:63). Paul echoed this power that resides in the Word of God: "For the Word of God is quick, and powerful" (Heb. 4:12).

Christians have long recognized the power of the Word of God. Faith, courage, joy, and energy are automatically encouraged to their maximum among people who commit these treasures to their memory, and repeat them daily. It's almost impossible to go away from a Bible study session without feeling a new burst of inspiration and energy.

TAKE A COLD SHOWER

This advice seems a little humorous to some people because it's usually given to those whose sexual desires have been aroused. But cold water is a great energizer. Few things will clear out the cobwebs and wake us up so easily as a dose of cold water. It can even help alleviate the pain of a depression. And it can certainly get those "slow starters" going in the morning.

It's usually not a good idea to jump right into a cold shower. Warm water is relaxing and comforting; it helps free us from tension and promotes a feeling of well-being. For those reasons it's a good idea to start off with a warm shower. Then when you're good and relaxed, you can gradually turn the warm water down until the water is as cold as you can stand it. Stay under it as long as you can and then turn the warm water back on. You may need to do this several times, but I'll guarantee you that it will make you feel alert and energetic.

One caution: Some people advocate that you finish off the shower with cold water. I haven't found this advice useful. Cold water inhibits circulation and, for some people, promotes tension. I've found it's better to end the shower with warm water. Stay under several minutes in order to get the blood flowing freely. The energizing effects of the cold water won't be counteracted by the relaxing effects of the warm water.

TAKE CAT NAPS

For those who are able to take them, short naps are a great way to recharge you with energy. Tired, tense workers or homemakers will usually profit from a few minutes spent on the couch, free from distractions. Even if you don't go to sleep, the benefits of lying down for a few minutes and suspending all cares are well worth it.

The daily cat nap is a much better way to handle tension than tranquilizers, alcohol, or sedatives. After a short nap (and I emphasize the word short) you often feel a surge of energy. I've found that creativity is enhanced after a nap. A short nap after work may make the remainder of the evening more enjoyable. The father who comes home from work too tired to interact with his family would profit from a quick nap before dinner (his family would profit as well). He would no doubt be more enjoyable to interact with, and he in turn would enjoy his family more.

For the person who is driven on by tension and emotional energy, the daily cat nap would probably prolong his life. This person is highly prone to heart attacks. By suspending all drive and tension for a few minutes each day, he would both increase his immediate energy and extend his productive years into later life.

People differ in their need for and ability to tolerate naps during the day. A few people say that they can't take any naps without disturbing their nightly sleep patterns. Others report that they are simply unable to go to sleep during the day unless they're exhausted. For these people a nap may be unrealistic. But even lying down for a few minutes and relaxing as completely as possible should be of benefit to them. When you lie down your heart works less; you save around twenty heartbeats a minute. This practice adds up over the years. It has both immediate and long-term benefits.

MAKE USE OF THE PRIVILEGE OF PRAYER

Prayer has many recognized benefits. Besides the obvious advantage of spiritual growth, strength, and communion with God it also promotes physical and mental health. "I can be exhausted, fed up, feeling like I can't take any more, but then after thirty minutes of prayer these feelings are

replaced by a spirit of faith, courage, and peace."
This is a common testimony of people who pray.
Many people wonder how those who don't pray
are able to maintain their sanity. One woman
said, "If I weren't a praying Christian I'd have
had a breakdown years ago."

Prayer has emotional, as well as spiritual,
benefits. To some extent, mental states such as
depression, guilt, despair, and dejection are
emotional disorders. But to a large extent they
are also spiritual disorders. Prayer helps alleviate
these experiences. It puts us in touch with divine
strength. It frees our energy—energy that is
being used up by these negative emotions—for
use in more constructive activities. It replaces
these energy-depleters with such energy-
enhancers as faith and courage. The person who
prays often is likely to find the energy he needs
to meet any task. Christ frequently spent all night
in prayer, and he suffered no energy loss because
of it. If he needed that kind of prayer, how much
more do you and I need it!

CHAPTER SIX
FIVE STEPS TO
LIFELONG ENERGY AND VIGOR

In the last chapter I offered six suggestions for getting a quick dose of energy when you need it. In this chapter I'd like to make five suggestions that should prove helpful to those who wish to promote long-term energy and vitality. These are ways to maintain your allotted supply of vital energy so that you'll have plenty with which to work, fight off disease, and be vigorous and healthy even into the later years. Some of these may surprise you; others are just common-sense suggestions.

EAT ONLY TWO MEALS A DAY

The habit of eating three meals a day is so strongly imbedded in American culture that many people believe there must be an innate need for three meals. This is simply untrue. From a historical point of view, three meals is a relatively modern cultural contrivance. Our early ancestors ate only two meals a day (sometimes only one). And in most cultures in the world today, especially in primitive societies, the preference is for two meals.

The habit of eating three meals a day began around 200 years ago. European aristocratic women initiated the shift to three meals when they began drinking a cup of chocolate in the morning, upon arising. Up to that time people didn't eat breakfast as we know it. They had a meal at about 10:00 A.M., and then another around 5:00 or 6:00 P.M. Soon this habit of taking chocolate in the morning changed into one of eating a full meal in addition to lunch and dinner.

This was a major step backward in diet. It put us out of step with both primitive peoples today and those strong, hardy folks of ancient times. According to both the Old and New Testaments, God's chosen people ate only two meals a day. As Dr. Herbert M. Shelton observes in his book, *Health for the Millions,*[1] both the Greeks and the Romans, most of whom could have made a fortune "as a modern athlete," ate two (and sometimes only one) meals a day. The Greeks ate a moderate meal at midmorning and then their biggest meal just before sunset. The Romans, upon arising, drank a glass of water. Then in the late morning they ate some fruit and cold meat. Their biggest meal was eaten in the early afternoon. Both upper and lower classes followed this regimen.

These hardy people didn't suffer from such frugal practices. On the contrary, they were extremely energetic and vigorous. The men from both armies could march for days under a heavy load of iron weaponry, clothes, and other provisions. Other energetic peoples such as the Hunzas, who live to be well into their hundreds, also eat fewer than three meals a day (and have enforced fasts when food is not available). Contrary to the popular slogan that we must eat to keep up our strength, these peoples seemed stronger and more energetic *because they didn't eat so often.*

As Dr. Shelton points out, frequent eating "places demands on the enzyme-secreting cells of both the mouth and stomach before they have recovered from their prior work period." Three meals, he goes on to say, makes them work constantly.

Other experts agree. Dr. Jean Mayer, for example, questions the practice of eating a big breakfast, despite the fact that we are told it is necessary if we are to be abundantly energetic. Dr. Mayer is a professor of nutrition at Harvard and a widely quoted food expert. As we look around the world today, Dr. Mayer observes, "we see that our three meals a day is the exception rather than the rule and that the first meal of the day, in particular, is extremely variable."[2]

Eating three meals a day is especially common in countries that rely on much refined food. Hamburgers, French fries, white bread, soft drinks, and other such junk foods provide few nutritional benefits; but they make people feel the need of more frequent meals. This habit of overeating junk food leads to degenerative diseases, and America is currently the world's leader in degenerative diseases. We could easily improve our health and vitality by eating fewer meals and filling our plates with higher-quality foods.

One of the greatest benefits of the two-meal-a-day plan is the great amount of vital energy it preserves. Energy is used up by the process of digestion. Blood has to go to the stomach, and enzymes are used up. The amount of vital energy used is, of course, quite small during a single meal. But over the years that amount builds up. It usually takes about five or six hours for the average meal to digest. This means that if you eat three meals a day, your stomach will be working every single minute of your working day, and a good bit at night as well. It never gets a chance to rest. Vital energy is continuously used up; it has no opportunity to replenish itself.

I believe that our national obsession with "irregularity," a rare obsession in other countries, is in part a result of the heavy demands we place upon our stomachs. Food is digested first in the stomach and then in the small intestine. The three-meal-a-day plan means that both stomach and small intestine have to work at the same time. The body has to supply blood to both organs simultaneously. As Sylvester Graham opined, the natural procedure is for the stomach to digest the food first, then pass it on to the small intestine. As the small intestine does its work, the stomach is free to rest. He believed that many of our "dietary irregularities" were caused by the practice of dumping food into the stomach at the same time the small intestine was working. This is why over the years the three-meal-a-day plan leads to disease and a great loss of vital energy. The stomach (and body) never effectively recoups its energy losses. For this reason the advice of such "experts" as Adelle Davis ("eat a little but often") is downright harmful.

So if you want to preserve your vital energy into later life—if you want to remain vigorous and healthy, and use your energy for more important things than constant eating—then eat only one or two meals a day, no more. I've observed that people who've followed this practice are, in old age, healthier, more alert and energetic, and less often senile than those who become "eating machines."

And there are other, secondary, advantages to the two-meal-a-day plan. Among them are the following:

1. *You're better able to resist disease.* When you switch from three meals to one or two meals a day, vital energy is freed for other uses. This energy, which would have been used up in the process of digestion, can be used instead by the body to clear out poisons and wastes, and to fight off diseases. This was one of the most obvious results I observed when I switched from three to two meals a day. Much of my energy seems now to be used to nip illness in the bud. I was the first in my family to switch to two meals. My wife kept eating three meals a day. In the past, we tended to give one another colds and viruses. But after switching to two meals, I found

that I didn't get as many illnesses and colds as she did. Everyone in the family would get them but me. This worked so well that my wife shifted to two meals a day. Now she is sick less often.

Immediately after you eat, especially if it is a large meal, there is a draft or pull on your energy. This is especially noticeable if you have to concentrate at some task. If your body is fighting off an infection, this pull on your energy may weaken you enough for the infection to win the battle. I noticed this one Christmas when we were visiting my parents. I had become ill with some virus that produced both respiratory and gastric symptoms. As a result, I practically stopped eating, and was in the process of overcoming it. Since my stomach felt much better, one evening I felt hungry, so I grabbed a large bag of pecans and began eating them (nuts are very hard to digest). I knew it was a mistake immediately after I did it, as I felt weaker right away. The next day I had a serious relapse, and was even sicker than I had been before. I had rechanneled my vital energy from its job of fighting the disease, and wasted it digesting a lot of nuts. And I paid the price for the indulgence.

I've seen other people pay the price also. I have some friends, a lovely couple with three children, who are really into health foods. They have sworn off sugar and junk food. They eat mainly raw foods, whole grains, and they take massive doses of vitamins. Their children also follow this regimen. The entire family's diet is almost perfect. *And yet the children are constantly ill.* They always seem to have colds, diarrhea, or some kind of affliction. And when they become sick, their illnesses last for weeks, sometimes months. The reason for their constant sickness is obvious. The mother is a fine woman. But she has unfortunately come to equate love and nurturance with indulgence. She feeds them constantly.

They eat only one meal a day, but it lasts the entire day. They eat breakfast, lunch and dinner and three snacks. Then, whenever their mother wants to reward them for something or show her love, she will say, "Do you kids want something to eat?" In all other respects their dietary practices are almost perfect, but this one habit is wrecking their health. I'm afraid that by the time these children become adults, they will be too weakened and enfeebled to enjoy a lifetime of energy, health, and vitality.

So if you want to enhance your body's ability to fight off diseases, switch to the two-meal-a-day plan. The German philosopher Arthur Schopenhauer ate only one meal a day for sixty years. And he wasn't sick for a single day during those sixty years. Maybe the same practices would work just as successfully for you.

2. *You get more done.* Obviously, if you eat two meals a day you have more time to do other things than you would if you ate three meals a day. If it takes you a half an hour to eat breakfast, that means you save three and a half hours a week by skipping one meal. That's just the amount of time saved by the person who would have eaten the meals. Think about the amount of time saved by the person who would have

prepared the meals. As a result of our two-meal-a-day plan, my wife has much more time available to do some things she wants to do. And, she says, "I put more into each meal now. Since I have to cook fewer meals, I try to make each meal better and more attractive."

I find that the two-meal-a-day plan enables me to get more done for another reason. Not only do I have more time, but I'm able to get right to work very soon after I arise in the morning. I find that what I do during the first couple of hours in the morning tends to set the pattern for the rest of the day. If I dawdle and procrastinate in the morning, I'll usually dawdle and procrastinate during the afternoon and evening. But if I work efficiently during the morning, I'll usually work efficiently in the remainder of the day. To me, breakfast is a form of dawdling. I especially feel that way now that I know that breakfast is unnecessary. When I get up I'm raring to go, to get busy. But before, when I ate breakfast, I had to curb my drive for the half hour or longer that it took for breakfast to be served and eaten. Now, immediately after shaving and dressing, I'm able to plunge right into work—writing, reading, grading papers, etc. I generally work for two or three hours like this before eating. So by the time 10:30 or so rolls around I've gotten a jump on the entire day. I've completed the most difficult tasks of the day (for most people, energy and courage levels are higher in the morning) and I've established a pattern that will carry me through the rest of the day.

3. *Eating is more enjoyable.* Food tastes better

to me now that I eat only two meals a day. When I ate three meals a day, the last meal didn't taste very good. I wasn't really hungry, and so I didn't enjoy it very much. Now I relish every meal.

4. *Your eating habits can improve.* Eating two meals a day can improve your health in ways other than freeing your energy to fight infection and dispel wastes and poisons. For one thing, you can drink more water. When you eat three meals a day there's really no time to drink water without interfering with the process of digestion. Water is one of the great fatigue fighters. Several years ago studies were done on fatigue in rats. As part of the experiment one group of rats was forced to drink massive doses of water. The other group was not. Then both groups were placed, one rat at a time, in a barrel of water to see how long they could swim. The rats who had been forced to drink water were able to swim much longer than the other rats. When you eat two meals a day you have more opportunities to douse your system with this "magic" elixir. In fact, drinking cool water is a good way to fight off "hunger pains" that sometimes come when you first switch to this program.

Another advantage is that you can eat the last meal of the day at an earlier time. Eating a late supper is a particularly bad habit. It causes you to sleep poorly and restlessly, and to wake up with foul breath, fatigue, a coated tongue, and often with headaches. If you eat the last meal earlier, your food digests by the time you go to bed, and none of these things happen.

5. *You are better able to control obesity.* At

least two or three times a year some new crash dieting book hits the best-seller list. Such books generally promise much and deliver little. The people who follow them may lose weight initially, but they usually seem to gain it back later.

The reason is that a "crash-diet" is not what's needed; a complete change in eating habits is. The two-meal-a-day plan is particularly helpful to the obese, especially if they eat two small meals. The easiest meal to skip is the first meal. And the longer you put if off, the easier it becomes to wait even longer before eating. So, for the obese person, I would offer the following advice: Do like Schopenhauer. Eat only one meal a day. And eat that meal in the early evening instead of the morning or afternoon. This continuous, lifelong diet would help you keep weight under control much more efficiently than a crash diet; and it would preserve your energy and health as well. Also, I think that mothers should put any child they suspect may have an obesity problem on the two-meal-a-day plan as early in life as possible. The key to controlling weight is to form good day-to-day eating habits. And the earlier those habits are formed, the easier it will be to stick with them.

6. *You can improve your spiritual experience.* In the Bible fasting is recommended in several places as a way to enhance spiritual perceptions. One reason for its effectiveness, I believe, is that it represents a control of the appetites. Many (even most) human sins are committed in the name of appetite. But the person who fasts is learning to control his appetites. The two-meal-a-

day plan does the same sort of thing. It allows you to gain greater control over yourself. The self-discipline acquired in this manner soon spreads to other areas, as you find it easier to discipline yourself in any practice. And, finally, eating less often makes you more spiritually perceptive. You can't hearken unto the voice of God as easily on a full belly as you can when the stomach is empty. I've seen many people fall asleep during sermons at church. Most of them seem to be overfed.

EAT BALANCED MEALS

There is little you can do, from a nutritional or dietary point of view, to increase your immediate energy level *as long as you are eating properly.* I realize that this statement flies in the face of much popular writing on energy—suggestions that "energy milkshakes," vitamin supplements, protein wafers, and other such energy foods are needed. As long as you follow two simple eating suggestions, the chances are that none of these miracle foods will actually help your energy level. These two eating suggestions, or principles, are: 1) Eat a variety of foods, or in other words, well-balanced meals, and 2) eat foods in their natural or unrefined states.

Nature has provided us with an abundant supply of all the nutrients we need. If you sample broadly from that supply, you probably won't need any supplements.

Specifically, there are seven basic food groups. They are: 1) green and yellow vegetables;

2) citrus fruits, tomatoes, cabbage; 3) potatoes, other vegetables and fruits; 4) milk and milk products, such as cheese; 5) meat, poultry, fish, eggs, dried peas, beans; 6) whole grain, flour, and cereals; 7) butter and fortified margarine. The rule to follow, if you want all the energy that food can provide is: *Eat a small amount from each of these groups every day rather than a large amount from only a few of the groups.*

THE CASE FOR AND AGAINST VITAMIN SUPPLEMENTS

There is still an unresolved debate over the importance of vitamin supplements. Some advocates of vitamin supplements believe that everyone should take them. I will briefly report the arguments pro and con and let you make up your own mind.

Advocates of vitamin supplements argue that although in times past a well-balanced meal took care of all nutritional needs, today's modern life style has made it difficult to meet all nutritional needs even if you try. For one thing, food is cooked in such a way as to deplete nutrients. This is especially true in restaurants, where food is made to taste pleasant rather than be nutritious. Much food is overcooked, a process which destroys vitamins and minerals (only steam-cooking, they point out, effectively preserves these nutrients, and few places steam-cook their vegetables). Even the average housewife sends a tremendous amount of nutrients down the drain when she pours out cooking water. Further, such experiences as stress—so common in the modern world—cause our bodies to use up its nutrients at a faster pace. If you are standing on a street corner and a car comes by, you breathe in its exhaust fumes. These fumes eat up vitamin C, as does cigarette smoke. Sugar also destroys the B vitamins. And salt eats up nutrients as well. So, they point out, even if vitamins won't always give you a quick lift, they still insure that you will have all the nutrients you need at any given time. They insure, in short, that you won't have to "borrow" into your body's vital reserves for energy.

Opponents of vitamin supplements point out that if you eat plenty of raw foods, and a well-balanced diet, vitamin supplements will be a waste of money. They assert that besides the enthusiastic testimonies of some individuals, most of the research has not supported the supposed benefits of vitamin supplements. Further, they argue that there are still many as yet undiscovered nutrients that vitamins won't supply you with. Finally, they point out that massive doses of some vitamins, particularly A and D, may actually be harmful, especially to unborn children.

For my purposes, vitamins are simply an insurance policy. As long as I eat well, keep a happy frame of mind, and avoid junk foods I probably don't need them. But somtimes I don't follow those practices. For those times I take vitamin supplements.

MAINTAIN CLOSE,
LOVING FAMILY RELATIONSHIPS

Until recently, social scientists had little understanding of the implications that warm family relationships have in almost every area of life. But today a mass of research has been conducted which demonstrates that loving family relationships promote mental health, happiness, physical health, and even long-term vital energy. These are just the benefits that adults enjoy. For children, a close knit family is even more important.

Several years ago a group of social scientists studied the heart disease rate among some Philadelphia residents.[3] The area they studied was a high-risk residence for heart disease. There was a lot of noise, air pollution, poor dietary habits, and the individualistic struggle for "more." As a result, the heart disease rate in that area was extremely high. However, the researchers located a group of recent Italian-American emigrants to America, now living in this high-risk area, whose heart disease rate was very low—lower in fact, than the national average. At first the reason for this was obscure. All the men were overweight; the diets were very high in cholesterols; they all lived in a high-risk area. But the thing that stood out among the Italian-Americans was the warm, loving family relationships they all enjoyed.

Several years later the researchers went back to this community to gather followup data. Interestingly, they found only one important change since the first time they visited: the

Italian-American family system had become less closely knit and loving. These people had adopted the practices and attitudes of those around them: success at any cost, family schisms, divorce, and quarrels. And as a result their heart disease rate had increased until it was higher than that among members of the community as a whole.

There is a power in a loving family relationship that is similar to the power of God's love. It can prolong life and even ward off diseases. A team of psychologists recently administered a battery of personality tests and life history questionnaires to a group of cancer patients at several hospitals.[4] They then compared the cancer patients (they all had tumors, to be exact) with a matched sample of people the same age but without tumors. The one difference between the two groups that stood out was this: *the cancer patients consistently had come from homes marked by divorce and unhappiness.* Certainly love is a powerful force if it can make us more resistant to disease. And the most important place where love can (or should) be found is in the home.

If you are unconvinced of the important implications that loving family relationships have for vital energy, consider the results of research comparing married men with single, divorced, and widowed men.[5] When compared with those three groups, married men, it was found, commit suicide less often, are less susceptible to mental illnesses and neuroses, have a much lower heart disease rate, and live to be a lot older. But the advantages don't stop there. Married men are also more energetic and productive. Married students, for example, earn higher grades than single students, even when the latter are more intelligent. Married men work harder, earn more money, are more punctual, pay their debts on time more often, and are generally more stable. Not surprisingly, married men report that they are happier than single men.

So if you want to be productive, energetic, healthy, and emotionally stable, and if you want to live to a ripe old age, take pains to insure that your family relationships are strong and loving. It will pay you great dividends in vital energy.

KEEP YOUR BLOOD CIRCULATING

Blood is the life force. All parts of your body must have free access to it if you are to be healthy and energetic. Your organs must have oxygen. And the way they get it is through the blood. The more efficiently the blood circulates, the more oxygen your organs will receive, and the healthier they will be. One of the major contributors to efficient circulation is activity.

Americans, according to physiological studies, are becoming flabbier and less physically fit. This muscle degeneration is not taking place only among the elderly. It is occurring with increasing frequency among the young. This trend has been getting worse and worse. In the last war, for example, pathologists conducted autopsies on many of the young men who had been killed in battle. They found that at least half had acquired advanced arteriosclerosis, a disease usually reserved for older people. It meant that many of our young men were physically unfit, their organs and muscles not receiving adequate oxygen. This is one reason why over 50 percent of all deaths in this country are due to diseases of the heart and blood vessels.

Adequate exercise is one of the best ways to protect the heart and blood vessels from rapid degeneration. Its benefits are profound. Exercise increases circulation, insures an adequate supply of oxygen, strengthens muscles, promotes resistance to disease, helps you sleep better, improves digestion, and promotes an attitude of confidence, alertness, and activity. From what I've witnessed, I believe that exercise even improves spiritual perceptiveness; you rarely hear of a flabby saint. It certainly improves mental fitness, as the increased supply of blood and oxygen to the brain helps sharpen the mind.

In trying to decide upon an exercise program, don't overlook the benefits of simple walking. I doubt that many of us need to engage in highly strenuous exercises in order to be healthy. In fact, that may be bad for you, from a vital energy standpoint, because it tends to make you feel tired and unmotivated the next day. Walking is a great exercise because it promotes better blood circulation and at the same time *it rests the heart.* When we walk, or use our legs in a similar manner, the blood is pushed upward by the legs into the heart. In fact, about 30 percent of the blood circulation is controlled by the legs when we walk. This allows the overworked heart to rest. Some doctors advise that a pace of four miles an hour for about one hour of walking should be sufficient.

There are, of course, many other exercises that you can choose from. Swimming, golf, tennis, and jogging are all beneficial. The main things to keep in mind as you choose a form of exercise are: 1) Keep it simple—don't construct a complex regimen; the more complex it is, the less likely you'll be to stick with it. 2) Do it regularly—walking every day is preferable to playing five vigorous sets of tennis on the weekend only. 3) Choose exercises that involve dynamic movement. I like weight lifting, but by itself it won't help the heart, lungs, and circulation as will more dynamic exercise. Choose an exercise that requires your legs to move. That insures that your heart will be strengthened and your circulation improved.

GET PLENTY OF SLEEP

Sleep patterns vary from one person to the next. True, the average person needs about seven to eight hours of sleep a night, but quite a bit of variation exists around that average. Some people need as much as ten or eleven hours in order to feel rested (studies do indicate that highly creative people tend to sleep longer than the average); others get by fine on three or four hours. A recent television special found a few people who got by on as little as fifteen minutes of sleep a night. They could not sleep much beyond that without feeling bad.

The most important thing is to find your own

best sleep pattern and adhere to it. Apparently, losing sleep causes our bodies to draw upon their vital energy reserves. If sleep is lost over several nights, the loss of vital energy may be irreplaceable. If the loss occurs over a long enough period, the brain may be damaged. But even mild losses of sleep slow down reaction time and impair judgment.

Research on sleep has uncovered four stages we all pass through as we doze. The deepest stage of sleep is the one during which we dream. Brain waves change as we move from one stage to the next. These changes in brain activity allow us to draw some conclusions about what goes on as we sleep through the night.

The first stage is one of light sleep. It occurs during the first ten or so minutes after we drift off. We tend to think about the events that have taken place during the day as we become gradually more relaxed. During stage two we become unaware of our surroundings. Images tend to run together and the eyes tend to move back and forth from one side to another. Stage three brings about almost complete relaxation. Some people toss and turn and others talk during this stage. Stage four plunges the sleeper into a state of total relaxation.

After the sleeper has been in stage four for a while he doesn't wake up. Instead, he gradually passes back into stage three, then stage two. This cycle takes about an hour and a half (on the average) and a person may pass through four or five such cycles during the night. There will be some important differences, however, between a person's sleep during stage two in the first cycle, and his behavior at that same stage in the other cycles. The person will not awaken so easily in the later stages, and his eyes, instead of gently moving back and forth, now bounce back and forth very quickly. For this reason the later cycle is called REM (Rapid Eye Movement) sleep. This is the phase during which most remembered dreaming takes place.

This period of REM sleep is very important for energy level, among other things. In one study the researchers monitored the brain waves of groups of sleepers they were observing.[6] Whenever the subjects went into REM sleep a buzzer would wake them up. After just one night of this the subjects reported feeling grouchy and irritable during the day. They worked at a much slower pace than normal and their self-confidence and vitality were reduced. When they were no longer awakened by the buzzer, the researchers observed that the subjects remained in REM sleep for much longer periods than usual. It's as if they were making up for lost sleep. These studies further indicate that it takes several nights of uninterrupted sleep to make up for the loss of REM sleep.

One final aspect of sleeping patterns that should be mentioned is the enemy of sleep: insomnia. It's estimated that about one half of the American population suffers from occasional insomnia. An estimated 30 million are chronic insomniacs. There are probably many reasons for this proliferation of sleeping disturbances. The great increase in sugar consumption may account for part of the trend. Sugar destroys both calcium and some of the B vitamins. These nutrients are important for sleep in that they both promote relaxation. (This may be a good reason to take vitamin and mineral supplements.)

The noise that permeates big cities and major highways frequently makes it difficult for some people to sleep peacefully. A few well-timed automobile horns may elevate the level of emotional energy high enough to prevent a relaxed frame of mind. Another contributor is work that requires prolonged concentration. This may make it hard for many people to allow their minds to relax and their attention to drift. Insomnia rarely afflicts those whose work requires dynamic body movements. It is usually associated with mental work.

There are several things that can be done to combat insomnia. Here are some suggestions:

1. Get plenty of calcium and vitamin B. There's plenty of calcium in milk (that's why warm milk is recommended by many doctors), but if you dislike milk you can get calcium tablets. The same goes for vitamin B supplements.

2. Exercise regularly. Dynamic exercise of some sort is a must for peaceful sleeping. One warning though: Don't exercise right before going to bed. That gets you too invigorated. Take your exercise at least two hours before bedtime.

3. Avoid late eating. Snacks eaten late at night, or heavy meals taken in the evening interfere with peaceful sleep. If you eat a heavy supper, eat it as early in the evening as possible. And if you get that "nervous hunger" before bedtime,

drink some cold water.

4. Avoid drugs, stimulants, alcohol and caffeine. All of these interfere with restful sleep. Even the so-called relaxants produce an eventual low. And the sleep they produce is not the most restful type.

5. Take a warm bath. Warm water relaxes you. And a warm bath is a better relaxant than a warm shower.

6. Don't worry about your insomnia. Some people work themselves up so much over a little insomnia that they just prolong what would have been a temporary problem. There's an advantage to simply lying awake in a restful frame of mind.

7. Get up and read a book. When all else fails, consider the possibility that you don't need as much sleep as you thought. You may benefit more from doing some reading (as long as it's not the stimulating kind) than you would from tossing and turning in bed.

NOTES

1. Herbert M. Shelton, *Health for the Millions* (Chicago: Natural Hygiene, 1968).
2. Jean Mayer, "Breakfast—Who Needs It?" *Family Health*, September, 1973.
3. Cited in Rudolf H. Moos, *The Human Context: Environmental Determinants of Behavior* (New York: Wiley, 1976).
4. Jerome D. Frank, "The Medical Power of Faith," *Human Nature*, August, 1978.
5. George F. Gilder, *Naked Nomads: Unmarried Men in America* (New York: Quadrangle, 1974).
6. Cited in Linda Pembrook, *How to Beat Fatigue* (New York: Doubleday, 1975).

CHAPTER SEVEN
THE THREE MAIN SOURCES OF ENERGY

This chapter title is a little misleading. Actually there are four main sources of energy. I purposely left "love" out of this chapter because an entire chapter is devoted to it later on in the book.

The three sources of energy covered in this chapter are emotion, sex, and aggression. All three are said to be "drives." There is an emotional drive, a sexual drive, and an aggressive drive. The word "drive" has been defined by psychiatrists and psychologists as "a strong motivating tendency that prompts activity toward a particular end." A popular definition of drive is "energy; push; initiative." Both these definitions convey the concept of a motivating force, or a source of energy. So we can speak in terms of emotional energy, sexual energy, and aggressive energy.

Everyone knows what it feels like to be in a state of high emotional arousal. Usually this occurs when we find ourselves in an anxiety-arousing situation, such as having to give a speech. Activity level increases; it's difficult to sit quietly or to relax. Heart rate increases. Blood pressure goes up. Breathing becomes fast and shallow. It's hard to concentrate. In short, the body is programmed for activity. And emotion is the source of energy for that activity.

This energy state has been called by a variety of names other than emotion: arousal, emotionality, drive, and anxiety, to name a few. While these terms seem to be describing different experiences, psychological research demonstrates that they are all referring to the same thing. Individuals who are highly anxious may be said to be high on arousal, drive or emotionality. Those who are low in anxiety may likewise be said to be low on drive, arousal, or emotionality. The source of the emotional energy in all cases has been traced to the autonomic nervous system.

Emotion is potentially one of the most useful or one of the most uncomfortable sources of energy. Highly emotional people have at their disposal quite a source of energy and drive, if they learn to channel and refine their emotions. But if they fail to come to grips with their emotions, if they fail to learn coping strategies for dealing with their emotional energy, they can easily develop a clinical neurosis that keeps them from effectively developing their strengths.

This idea that powerful emotions, even neurotic emotions, are not necessarily bad in themselves is clearly evident in a study conducted with highly creative writers as subjects. In this study both highly creative writers and average writers were given a personality test that was sensitive to both neurotic and psychotic emotions. The highly creative writers, it was discovered, scored above the average writers on those parts of the test that pick up both neurotic *and* psychotic emotions. So according to this study, gifted, imaginative writers have very powerful, and not always healthy, emotions. In fact, their emotions hardly differ at all from those of very neurotic or even psychotic individuals. The main difference is that the creative writers have learned to control and channel their emotions—in short, they've learned to *use* their emotions—while the neurotics allow themselves to be used *by* their own emotions. Looking at the results of his own study, the researcher observed that, "from these data one might be led to conclude that creative writers are, as the common man has long suspected them to be, a bit 'dotty.' "[1]

But "dottiness" shows up about as frequently in gifted persons as it does in disturbed persons. Charles Darwin, for example, was so emotional and high strung that he could hardly bear to talk to strangers. One time he became so excited about a letter he had just written to a friend that he couldn't sleep all night. Modern psychologists might call him a textbook neurotic. But this simply illustrates the principle that what may turn into a serious personality flaw in one person or under some conditions may actually be a gift in another person or under different conditions. Emotional energy fits this description. It's either a valuable force or a curse, depending upon how it's used.

Origins. Whether you have a lot or a little emotional energy depends to a great extent upon heredity. Studies have shown that children differ from one another on such measures of emotional drive as heart and respiration rate, blood pressure, etc., from the moment of birth. And twin studies—those comparing identical twins separated at birth and reared in different homes—show that level of emotional energy is strongly influenced by heredity. This does not mean that experience plays no role. A series of traumatic events in early childhood may serve to increase an individual's level of emotionality. But heredity still has a strong influence.

A description of the biological underpinnings of emotionality is not within the purview of this book. However, I should mention that emotional drive springs from biochemical processes. The autonomic nervous system—with its twin subsystems called the sympathetic and parasympathetic systems—plays a major role in the experience of emotionality. Adrenaline, a chemical produced in the sympathetic system, also has a central role in emotional activation.

Emotionality as a Drive. The concept of emotion as an energizing force is not new. Physiologists have long said that emotional arousal prepares us for "fight or flight." Emotional arousal, in other words, gives us a much-needed source of energy; much-needed in the sense that without it we would be unable to put forth the sort of effort necessary either to vigorously attack and defeat the fear-inducing object or flee from it with enthusiasm. In either case, aroused emotion makes it possible for us to do things we could not otherwise do.

The function of emotional arousal—that of producing energy—is recognized by many psychologists and physiologists. Consider, for example, the following statements from three psychologists:

There is no action without emotion.[2]

Man's intellect is an indispensable resource in his growth. . . . But he can advance no further than his inner force, his total emotional resources . . . can propel him.[3]

A person devoid of emotions displays very little activity, either mental or physical. . . . Strong emotions or, to be more exact, impatience may be responsible for gross errors of judgment, but without strong emotions there would be no intellectual achievement.[4]

To give you an idea of the energizing power of aroused emotions, consider an example that every homemaker can identify with. A young mother of two preschool children, a boy aged three months and a girl aged four years, has been up half the night with her three-month-old. On top of that she arose this morning at 7:00 to make breakfast for her husband. It's late morning. The older child is playing at a neighbor's house, and the baby has finally taken his nap. The mother is exhausted. The house is a wreck, but the last thing she feels like doing is cleaning it up. All she wants to do is stretch out on the sofa for a few minutes. The phone rings. The church treasurer, who also happens to be the resident gossip, has phoned to say that she will be by in a few minutes to pick up a donation this mother pledged to the church. All of a sudden, fatigue is forgotten. This "exhausted" mother jumps away from the phone and in an amazing display of energy and drive cleans the entire house (or at least the observable parts) in a matter of minutes. Where did all this energy come from? It came from her aroused emotions.

So emotions, when aroused, serve as a source of drive and energy. This suggests that highly emotional or anxious people have at their disposal a greater source of energy and drive than those who are more emotionally stable and less anxious. We tend to think that being an emotional person is a great disadvantage. And it's true that the highly emotional person has a greater chance of becoming neurotic than the unemotional person. But he also has a chance of being more productive and energetic if he can channel and make use of his emotions. So the highly emotional person who uses his emotions adaptively is actually better off in some ways than the emotionally stable person. Though he may say and do things impulsively, things that he would not say or do if he were less emotional, his emotions still give him an advantage in energy usage.

Here is one of the main differences between the adaptive, but highly emotional person and the neurotic: The neurotic allows his emotionality to work against him. He either bottles it up, allows it to be used up in pointless daydreaming, or withdraws from grappling with his world in order to avoid the sometimes uncomfortable experience of emotional arousal (in the form of anxiety). For some reason, he fails to make use of his emotions. Louis Bisch, in his classic book *Be Glad You're Neurotic,* recognizes the need to make adaptive use of the emotions. He even goes so far as to say that being a neurotic actually signifies that you have hidden strengths. One of those strengths is emotional energy:

Emotions, you see, must be expressed, turned loose, sometimes let run wild. They should be projected toward something. Otherwise . . . they keep you steaming and boiling; they weaken you; they wear you down to skin and bone. . . . When we're neurotic there is unrest inside us. Yet this unrest is merely the sign that we are gaited for better things; that we have not as yet found ourselves. The neurotic must learn to respect his condition; to understand it. He must cease being ashamed and afraid.[5]

I'll elaborate on this statement later on. My goal is to point out the adaptive features of high emotional drive and to offer advice for best dealing with and channeling emotional arousal. This one trait—emotionality—can result in higher productivity, creativity, and energy; or it can produce the opposite—stagnation, unhappiness, and neurosis. It all depends upon how it is managed.

Yerkes-Dodson Law. If emotionality serves as a drive state or motivating force, then it should be related to an individual's performance or level of productivity. Research has, in fact, consistently demonstrated the better performance of highly emotional individuals on a variety of tasks— memory tasks, arithmetic problems, fine muscle tasks, etc.—in the absence of pressure, and the better performance of emotionally stable individuals when pressure was present.

This is the famous Yerkes-Dodson Law. Simply stated, it goes like this: energy output (or productivity) is higher at moderate levels of emotional arousal; too little emotional arousal is associated with low performance, and too much arousal is likewise associated with low performance.

So according to this law, highly emotional individuals would, in their normal resting state, perform much better than emotionally stable persons. This is because highly emotional individuals operate at a moderate level of emotional activation, whereas emotionally stable individuals in their normal resting state are at too low a level of activation to be very productive; in other words, they are insufficiently emotionally aroused to perform adequately in day-to-day activities.

Experiments have verified the higher level of performance of emotional persons. For example, in one experiment, which required individuals to memorize pairs of words presented at four-second intervals, the highly emotional group made significantly fewer errors than the emotionally stable group.

However, when the interval between presentation of the word pairs was dropped from four seconds to two seconds, the number of mistakes increased drastically for the highly emotional group but remained about the same for the low emotional group. This illustrates another characteristic of the relationship between emotionality and performance: The less pressure there is in the performance situation, the better the emotional persons will perform; on the other hand, as pressure increases, the emotionally stable group will soon come to outperform the highly emotional group. The reason is obvious. Pressure increases emotional arousal. Without pressure the highly emotional person is at an optimum drive level. With increasing pressure, the highly emotional group becomes too aroused. Emotion begins to cloud judgment and performance. For the stable group, however, pressure moves them to the intermediate level of arousal, the optimum level for performance.

These findings have relevance for everyday living. Highly emotional persons generally perform better in their day-to-day activities than emotionally stable individuals. But once pressure is added, the emotional individual's performance plummets (unless he is exceptionally competent). This law seems to apply in all areas: at work, in social encounters, and at school. I have observed from my experience giving individual intelligence tests that highly emotional individuals tend to do much better on the untimed portions of the tests, and their performance tends to decline on the timed parts; for stable individuals the reverse applies.

Sara P. is a good example of a highly emotional individual who manages her life quite well in day-to-day activities and tends to do more poorly when pressures mount. An honor student in college, she held several office management jobs at which she had been given very high ratings. Once out of college, she was hired as a personnel assistant in the local office of a nationwide corporation.

Initially she was able to maintain a characteristically high level of performance. About four months after she began work there, however, the branch manager began to apply pressure to the personnel department because of a high turnover rate among the employees. The end result of this was that pressure was placed upon Sara to hire employees willing to accept low salaries and poor working conditions and yet be likely to remain on the job for long periods of time. Although this was an impossible task, Sara accepted it and set out to meet the demands. Needless to say, she was not successful. The pressures of the job affected her performance, which plummeted. Eventually she had to look for another job.

The Special Problem of Anxiety. Anxious people probably see little benefit in their uncomfortable emotion. High anxiety interferes with performance, makes us feel inadequate, and renders us powerless and helpless. Little benefit can be derived from these experiences.

However, anxiety is a form of emotional energy. The person undergoing a strong experience of anxiety is simply in a state of high emotional arousal—programmed for activity—and has come to conceptualize his emotional arousal in negative terms. If he possessed more self-confidence or had an expectation of imminent success, he might experience the emotional arousal in more positive terms.

To give you an idea of the possible benefits of anxiety (i.e., emotional energy), consider the results of studies which show a positive relationship between anxiety and creativity. The creative person discharges his emotions inwardly in the form of intense fantasies and mental images. Rather than acting out his emotions, the creative person inhibits them, keeps them from being discharged physically, and as a result, they erupt in the form of rich mental imagery that is so characteristic of creative persons. Their emotionality is channeled into mental activity rather than physical activity.

That this relationship between anxiety and creativity does exist is evident in several studies which demonstrate a correlation between high anxiety and performance on tests of originality, fantasy, and novelty. Psychologist Michael Wallach reviewed all of the studies that had been conducted on creativity. Based upon his review, Wallach concluded that highly anxious people are more creative than non-anxious people. They have, he observed, an "introspective sensitivity" that gives them a head start in originality, perceptiveness, and creativity.[6]

These findings seem to argue that the highly emotional person—including the very anxious individual—is a veritable breeding ground for mental imagery, spontaneous fantasy, and vivid mental activity. It is no wonder that so many of the creative intellects of this and other generations have often been anxious, even "neurotic," individuals.

So close is this relationship between emotionality and creativity that I've concluded that little in the way of truly creative work can be done without at least a moderate amount of emotional arousal. An example of this observation is seen in the work of psychiatrist George Crane, who wrote the syndicated column, "The Worry Clinic," for over twenty years. Here is a description of how he went about writing six columns a week for over twenty years and how he relied on emotional energy to galvanize him into creative effort:

. . . as the day arrives when my weekly "agenda" lists the fact that I must write my six daily "Worry

Clinic" articles for newspapers, here's the way I normally act.

During breakfast, I am vaguely irritable, for I am worrying about the choice of psychology cases to describe in those six daily articles.

I stall some more by reading the morning paper and my mail. Then I pick some case histories from my files. But I still try to avoid the hard work of phrasing my sentences at the typewriter. For instance, I may decide that my typewriter ribbon needs changing, so I gleefully perform that manual chore.

As long as I am doing something, even though it is manual and not requiring much thought, my conscience is vaguely appeased. Then I may oil the typewriter. By this time I imagine I am thirsty, so I get a bottle of pop or a cup of coffee.

To stall off the inevitable, I call my secretary downtown to find out what morning mail may be there at the office. Then I wander around looking at some of my books or glancing through medical and psychological journals.

Meanwhile, my thoughts are vaguely "polarizing" around the six cases which I wish to describe in my week's batch of copy. Often I thus squander so much time that it is almost noon, so I decide I might as well eat lunch first.

Obviously I grow more preoccupied and grouchy every minute. For I am becoming irate at Mr. Sloth and indulging in self-recrimination about the fact that the clock now shows 1 P.M.

After lunch, with no further excuse for stalling, I reluctantly sit down at my typewriter. It is only when my emotional ire reaches the eruptive or volcanic state that I can actually percolate mentally.[7]

There is a great danger that we will fail to properly channel and utilize this emotional energy. Sometimes we discharge it indiscriminately and other times we overinhibit it and then feel it turn inward to work against us. But if we know how to use emotional energy properly, it will serve us admirably in many different areas.

One use of emotional energy, suggested by Crane in the above quote, is a weapon against procrastination. Take writing, for example. A writer will desire to turn out much material and yet dread getting started. The problem is that the energizing force (the emotional drive) is no stronger than the inhibiting force (the fear of writing; laziness, etc.). Sometimes, in order to overcome the resulting standoff, it may be useful to put off writing for a while in order to let the emotion build up, as Dr. Crane did. You might even remind yourself that you *should* be writing, in order to increase your anxiety level even higher. Then when you finally sit down to write, your anxiety (emotional energy) level will be so high that the words will almost erupt onto the paper.

Emotionality and Rigidity. Emotionality serves to strengthen habits; so if two people—one high on emotionality and one low—form a habit, the highly emotional individual will feel more compelled to repeat that habit in a variety of situations, whether it be appropriate or not. Low emotionality gives a little more flexibility.

Hans Eysenck, using this principle of emotionality and habit formation, has offered an explanation of the oft-observed rigidity of emotional people. Highly emotional persons tend to get locked into rigid, self-perpetuating patterns. Eysenck suggests that this high emotionality causes them to form strong habits—that is, the skills they learn, they tend to cling to much more strongly. It's as if their great emotional energy cuts deep grooves in their habit patterns, making both appropriate and inappropriate habits stronger than in the non-emotional person. So when they are placed in a situation requiring a slightly different behavior from the one they've already learned, they find it hard to learn new habits. Studies of skill learning—in which individuals can win money for performing a certain learned skill—have shown that once highly emotional individuals learn a given skill, they tend to cling to it rigidly no matter how inefficient it becomes in other situations. Low emotional individuals, on the other hand, show much more flexibility in their ability to discard old skills and learn new ones. This no doubt accounts for much of the difficulty some highly emotional persons have in social situations; they tend to cling to old habits of relating to people no matter how unfruitful these habits have become.

I think this relationship between high emotionality and rigidity explains in part another maladaptive behavior pattern: fear of failure.

Some people have such extremely high goals for themselves that they feel they must always live up to. If they fall short of those standards even once, they punish themselves severely. (They often come from homes where one or both parents were overly punitive.) This puts them in a bind. They are motivated to attempt great things, and yet they fear failure. So they often settle the dilemma by trying to do such impossible tasks that no one could blame them if they fail. Thus they lock themselves into a self-destructive, self-perpetuating pattern. This pattern is reinforced by their high emotionality and resultant rigidity.

As a college teacher I've seen many students lock themselves into this destructive pattern. They will come into my office with a long schedule of courses they want to take, even though they may already be working a full-time job. I'll suggest that they take it easier and only take as many courses as they are sure they can successfully pass. They will insist that they can successfully pass this many. Then I watch them in the classroom. They are late turning work in. Even as late as the middle of the quarter they've hardly done anything. The smarter ones do the inevitable: they drop the course. The others go right on down into failure, insisting that they can get it done ("if only I didn't have to take so many courses"). When failure comes, their friends console them by saying, "You shouldn't try so much. You'll kill yourself." They console themselves by thinking, "I didn't really try my best on this one. If I really try next time, I can be successful." So they continue the pattern again, not learning from their mistakes.

I find that these persons are almost always highly emotional. Though the pattern they've created for themselves is easy to see, they still can't seem to break it. There is so much emotional energy invested in it that these habits and patterns defy logic and insight.

It's obvious from this discussion that high emotionality has both adaptive and nonadaptive features. On the adaptive side, the highly emotional person has quite a source of energy and activity at his disposal. He will likely feel driven at times. If he is forced to sit passively for any length of time, he will become restless and unhappy. Tension may build up. On the other hand, his fantasy level and mental vigor will be aided by the emotional energy. He will have the raw products of creativity—a lively imagination—available for use. In his daily activities also, he will be more productive and energetic than his less emotional friends. On the nonadaptive side, the person with much emotional energy will tend to perform more poorly under pressure than emotionally stable people. He will be more likely to get himself locked into rigid, self-perpetuating patterns. His spontaneity may suffer as a result of this greater emotional drive. Emotion may cause him to cling to some behaviors and ideas tenaciously, even when they no longer serve a purpose.

Managing Emotionality. Emotion is a powerful force. It can serve you well or it can turn against you, depending upon how you use it. One psychologist was able to study firsthand the phenomenon of "Voodoo death." That occurs when a witch doctor sticks a pin in the figure of a village member or places a curse upon him. The cursed person then goes home, lies down, and dies right around the time the witch doctor predicted. There's no supernatural force involved in the phenomenon, but the witch doctor does know how to recruit a powerful ally in his ritual of death. That powerful ally is his victim's emotionality.

Managing high emotionality depends upon the learning of two coping skills. In the first place, you should learn to channel emotional energy into effective behavior while at the same time avoiding rigidity. Some persons with much restlessness and a high state of arousal are able to so discipline themselves that the energy serves them well. Others find themselves being overwhelmed by their emotionality, locked into self-perpetuating patterns, or using their drive in useless daydreaming which serves the purpose of avoiding rather than dealing with reality.

Secondly, persons prone to experience emotional "overloads" need ways of dealing with anxiety during stressful experiences so that their performance will not be hampered by too much anxiety. Giving speeches, engaging in stressful competition, and taking part in harsh confrontations and altercations are all examples of events that may arouse the emotional person's anxiety too high for effective performance to be maintained. Reducing the level of anxiety during these experiences is the goal of this second section.

The Channeling of Emotion. High emotionality can energize performance on the job just as easily as it can energize anxiety or anger. Many people have had the experience of enhanced performance through channeled emotion. Athletes, rising to a high state of emotional arousal, have turned in almost superhuman performances, often accounting for last-minute victories. Some of the world's most beautiful poetry and songs have been written under a state of high, channeled emotion. For example, "The Star-Spangled Banner" was penned during the height of an intense battle; and H. G. Spafford limned the beautiful hymn, "It Is Well with My Soul," after learning of the tragic death of his wife and daughter. So when an individual finds himself in an emotionally arousing situation— one that calls for skillful performance—his major task is to channel his emotions so that they work for him rather than against him.

So how can emotional energy be rechanneled during the stressful event?

1. Learn to conceptually *relabel the feeling state.* Experiments have demonstrated that during a state of emotional arousal the actual feeling state that a person experiences depends upon how he labels or conceptualizes his state of activation. Psychologist Stanley Schacter conducted an experiment which demonstrated this relationship.[8] He told volunteers for his

experiment that he was interested in the effect of a vitamin on their vision, and they agreed to an injection of the vitamin. In actuality he injected them with epinephrine, a biochemical agent which mimics sympathetic system arousal; in other words, it produces a high state of emotional arousal. After the injection their blood pressure and heart rate increased, their respiration level went up, and they had tremors, flushing, and palpitations for a period of about twenty minutes.

During this period these subjects were placed in a room. In this room there was another person who supposedly was also a subject in the experiment; in actuality he was an actor performing a part. In one condition the actor behaved in a very euphoric manner; he chatted in a friendly and extroverted way; he played "basketball" with wastepaper and a garbage can, flew paper airplanes, made a slingshot, and played with a hula hoop. In the other condition, the actor behaved in a very angry manner. While sitting across a table from the subject, he filled out a questionnaire asking many personal questions. For a while, he made irritated statements about the personal questions asked of him on the questionnaire; soon his irritation turned to anger and eventually he jumped up, tore up the questionnaire, and rushed from the room in a state of outrage. The reactions of the persons who had received the injections were observed from a two-way mirror and they were subsequently given a questionnaire designed to measure their feelings.

While the details of the experiment are beyond

the scope of this book, suffice it to say that these subjects, who didn't know the reason for their state of emotional arousal, were heavily influenced by the situation in which they found themselves. Those exposed to the euphoric actor began to act in a euphoric manner themselves and reported greater feelings of euphoria and excitement. Those exposed to the angry actor reacted likewise with anger. Schacter concluded from his study that when a person finds himself in a state of emotional arousal and has no satisfactory explanation to account for his arousal, he will be highly influenced by explanations given to him.

His explanation seems to accord with my own observations. Two different individuals under the same degree of emotional arousal will respond with totally different feeling states and therefore perform totally different behaviors, depending upon their conceptualization or explanation of the situation. Take, for example, the situation of two persons about to make a public speech. Both are in a state of emotional arousal over the impending performance. But one conceptualizes the speech as a situation in which he will be exposed to the criticism of others, will likely make glaring mistakes, and will end up incurring the disapproval of his audience. The other person conceives of the speech in more positive terms: he sees it as an opportunity to display his skills and be appreciated for this display by an audience, and he expects that his performance will be successful. These two people with approximately equal speaking skills will likely perform in very different manners. The first will find it hard to speak, his associations will tend to block and be clumsy, his voice will quiver, and he will likely perform in a poor manner. The second will probably find his thoughts coming in a rapid, free manner, he will report positive feelings, and his performance will likely be smoother. The difference lies in the two conceptualizations of the same situation.

The person who conceptualizes the situation (and, possibly, emotional arousal itself) in negative terms will feel that his emotions are working against him, as a source of interference. The person who views the situation in more positive terms will undergo quite a different experience. The problem always becomes, in a state of activation, either to use the emotionality or be used by it.

Adolescents seem especially able to channel high emotional arousal through their strong identification with heroes. The budding young athlete will imagine himself as a Muhammed Ali, or a Walt Frazier, or Tom Seaver. The imitation sessions, during which the nascent superstar actually *becomes* his ideal, come naturally to adolescents. As yet they still lack a clear sense of identity; they are less inhibited, therefore, about "borrowing" the identity of another. As often as not, this role-taking charade acts as a disinhibitor, freeing the adolescent from the realities and restraints of his own less-heroic personality.

One young man related his experience using this method to me. "I had to give a short talk to the congregation at my church. Usually I do poorly when I have to talk before an audience; my voice quivers, and I am barely able to get the words out. I usually dread these talks, and this one was no different, except that my girl friend was present in the congregation. I was pretty nervous before walking up to the pulpit. But once I got up there, a funny thing happened. I began thinking about a preacher I used to admire, an evangelist. He was an excellent speaker, the kind that held an audience in the palm of his hand. And while I was thinking about him—this was right before I was supposed to give my talk—I started imagining that I was this preacher. I know it sounds funny, but I actually walked up to the pulpit the same way he always did. And I wasn't nervous a bit during my talk. Afterwards everybody told me how well I did. It was quite an experience."

Many actors report that they are shy and lacking in self-assurance until they play the role of a very confident person. Then they actually start to feel as they imagine that character would feel. Some comedians who use humorous "characters" say that these characters loosen them up and free blocked emotions. It's probably a shame that as adults we lose this ability to pretend that we are someone else. It would probably make quite a bit of difference in our performances during anxiety-provoking situations.

2. Read inspirational literature, *The Power of Positive Thinking,* or a similar book. I have experienced the benefits of a positive mental set during a stressful situation. As an amateur boxer,

I was quite anxious while awaiting the beginning of a match. Many boxers experience anxiety while awaiting a match. Novice boxers are especially prone to tremendous bouts with anxiety. In fact, many young boxers give the impression that they are in poor physical condition due to prolonged anxiety, so that when the fight finally rolls around, they are drained. Because of their lack of experience and negative frame of mind, the emotionality works to their disadvantage rather than sharpening their skills.

On two occasions, during the day of a boxing match, I passed the time by reading "inspirational" books such as *The Power of Positive Thinking* and *How to Stop Worrying and Start Living*. I noticed some years afterward— while reviewing my experiences as a boxer— that I had turned in my two best performances in those fights. In retrospect, I concluded that by reading these inspirational books, I had put myself in a positive, confident frame of mind, and this mental attitude had contributed to excellent performances. Now, whenever I have to do something that I do not feel confident about, I make it a habit to spend time before the dreaded event soaking up inspirational messages. I have even found that this method increases productivity and creativity.

Reducing Anxiety.

1. *Practice focusing the attention forcefully upon some object or event.* Studies have shown that when people focus their attention intently upon something—whether it be a picture, a sound, or

a mental image—their heart rate, their blood pressure, and their respiration rate tend to lower. Blotting out extraneous stimulation in this manner serves to distract us from our fears and anxieties.

This sort of intense concentration works well in stressful situations. When you are waiting to give a speech, for example, your anxiety level is usually very high if you are not used to public speaking. Many people have in fact, been discouraged from ever attempting public speaking because they cannot control their prespeech anxiety. Under severe anxiety, the voice may quiver, memory fails, and words come out in a choppy, incoherent manner, Focusing the attention intently upon some object brings the level of anxiety down. It doesn't matter what the object is, so long as you look long and hard at it or listen intently to it, to the exclusion of everything else.

I've found that this method works much better than the usual advice for reducing anxiety: relaxation techniques. While learning to relax is an important adjustment mechanism, it's not very effective in reducing immediate emotional arousal right before or during a stressful event. When emotions are aroused, the body is programmed for activity. Advice such as, "Practice releasing your legs, then your arms, then your chest, etc.," works in the opposite direction from arousal. This is a passive strategy, good for use in the quiet and calm of your own bedroom. It is not suitable for the time when your entire body and mind are programmed for effort. Concentrating—or actively focusing your attention, on the other hand—is an active process. It makes use of the arousal, instead of fighting against it.

2. As much as possible, *seek to master tasks that usually provoke strong anxieties.* As described above, the more completely a skill or task has been learned, the less likely is high emotional arousal to disrupt performance. The pianist who has learned a piece well, to the extent that he can almost play it in his sleep, will likely be aided by high anxiety during a public recital. The pianist who has just barely learned the same piece will likely find his performance disrupted under conditions of high emotional arousal.

So if you have to give a speech, and you fear that your anxiety will be too high to control, make sure that you have practiced and practiced it beforehand. Then when the time comes to give it, channel and control your emotional energy by concentrating (and possibly by pretending that you are some well-known, self-assured speaker). Learn to use your emotion for energy; don't be used by it.

SEXUAL ENERGY

Of all the sources of energy, the sexual drive is probably the most pervasive and profound. In general, the way in which the sexual drive is used determines the amount of energy, productivity, and creativity in a society more than any one single factor. As I'll show later on, cultures that require people to control their sexual energy are more "energetic" than those that allow it to be used up in promiscuous sexual relationships.

We who live in this culture don't need to be convinced about the pervasive influence of sexual energy. Most of our songs, movies, television programs, and books revolve around sexual themes. Even the Bible acknowledges the profound significance of sexual energy. Many of its symbols, metaphors, and analogies use sexual language. (I'm using the term "sex" in the broad sense of heterosexual relationships, marriage, childbearing, etc., not just in the sense of sexual intercourse.) Christ, for example, referred to himself as the "Bridegroom" and the Church as the "Bride" in order to reflect the deep intimacy that should exist between him and his people. When James wanted to describe the cause of sin, he referred to the process of impregnation and childbirth: "Then when lust hath conceived, it bringeth forth sin." John, in Revelation, described a bad church as a "harlot" and a good church as a "virtuous woman." These and many other similar verses throughout the Bible indicate that God used our most profound experience to communicate his principles and lessons to us.

There is a strong relationship between the way we handle our sexual drive and sexual relationships, on the one hand, and the amount of energy we have left over for such activities as work, productivity, problem-solving, and creativity. People who use up their sexual energy in promiscuous sexual relationships have less available for work and creativity.

This relationship between sexual control and productivity has been demonstrated in psychological studies. One experiment, for example, found that college students who were sexually chaste made higher grades than those who were promiscuous.

But probably the most convincing studies are those that compared the productivity of promiscuous cultures with that of more chaste cultures. British anthropologist J. D. Unwin did exactly that in a brilliant study of the sexual practices of over eighty different cultures.[9] He wanted to discover the reason why some cultures show so much energy and others show so little. So he divided these cultures up into four groups, from the least to the most productive and energetic; and he found that the most unproductive and lethargic cultures were those that allowed the greatest amount of sexual freedom. Cultures that we call "primitive" and "backward," in other words, are those that allow their young people to engage in promiscuous sexual relationships and their married adults to commit adultery. Cultures that required premarital chastity of their young people and postmarital fidelity of the married adults, on the other hand, had the greatest amount of energy and the most productive cultures. They were the ones that built advanced civilizations.

In addition to these findings, sociologist Pitirim Sorokin did a study several years ago in which he looked at the relationship between sexual practices and creativity.[10] Beginning with ancient Greeks and Romans, and continuing right up to the present, he counted the number of scientific creations and inventions that were made in each century. Then he compared that with the amount of sexual freedom that was allowed in that century. His findings: the number of scientific creations increased in those centuries in which less sexual freedom was allowed, and decreased during those centuries in which greater sexual freedom took place.

All of this suggests that God's plan for marriage and sexual behavior not only allows us to live more wholesome lives, it also gives us greater energy. Probably the most sexually chaste period in history was right after the Protestant Reformation. Luther, Calvin, and all the other reformers wrote extensively on the proper way to handle sexual urges. They preached that every man should restrict his sexual activity to his own wife. The result of this message is obvious: There followed the most creative and energetic period in the history of the world.

Most adults, particularly men, have urges for sexual activity outside the bonds of matrimony. If they refuse to indulge those urges, and instead restrict their sexual activity to their spouses, then a great surge of energy becomes available to them. This energy, which could have been used up in promiscuous sexual relationships, is instead available for work and creativity. This is the sort of energy that became available to Americans and Western Europeans after the Protestant Reformation. This energy is the main reason for the great Industrial Revolution that followed closely upon the heels of Puritanism.

It's a shame to see the doctrine of sexual freedom make such great inroads into American sexual practices. Besides contradicting Christian principles, it indicates a loss of energy, productivity, and creativity in the future. Some other nations, such as the sexually continent Japanese, are already in the process of surpassing us in their variety of technological inventions. There's no excuse for Christians following the practices of the remainder of the society, though. We've been given ample instruction in the Bible on how to handle the sexual drive. That instruction, if followed, would provide each of us (and the nation as well) with an abundance of energy and vitality.

AGGRESSIVE ENERGY

The word *aggression* can be simply defined from its Latin origin as a forward movement; to move forward. It connotes energy and initiative. Unfortunately, aggression is usually considered as something negative. Psychologists, in fact, have devoted much effort toward setting up programs designed to eradicate aggression. These programs generally involve implementing an environment for children which, supposedly, will wipe out any traces of this so-called harmful drive.

Sigmund Freud was one of the first scientists to define aggression in negative terms. Initially Freud thought that all human energy, including aggressive energy, stemmed from the sexual drive. In fact, for many years he saw no reason to postulate an aggressive drive separate from the sexual drive. No doubt this was a part of the cultural climate in which Freud lived. In nineteenth-century Vienna sexuality was considered something to be obscured and hidden, certainly not to be discussed in normal conversation. Wrapped up as he was in his theory of sexuality, Freud initially rejected the idea of a separate aggressive drive.

Eventually, however, Freud was forced to concede the existence of a separate aggressive drive. The occurrence of the First World War in Europe, followed by the rise of the Nazi party with its systematic prejudice, compelled Freud to integrate the aggressive drive into his theory of development.

Freud's acceptance of an aggressive drive in mankind was a breakthrough for psychoanalysis; but when Freud at last came to recognize that an innate aggressive drive existed, he thought of this drive as something negative. The theory that he eventually accepted (though he never seemed to be totally satisfied with it) was that two innate drives exist. One was a life-enhancing drive (which included the sexual drive); the other was a life-destroying, self-destructive drive. The latter Freud believed included the aggressive drive. Thus his theory postulated that mankind was born with self-destructive tendencies which were frequently projected outward onto the rest of the world, taking the form of war, crime, and violence.

Unfortunately, most other psychologists have followed Freud's lead and talked as if the aggressive drive were completely negative. The importance of aggressive energy in man's search for mastery of his world is rarely recognized.

God no doubt had a purpose in endowing mankind with aggressive energy, though the aggressive drive (like the sexual drive) has been often misused and misapplied. As we shall see later, there is ample evidence for the belief that without an aggressive drive human beings would be totally unable to master their environments, to learn efficiently, and to create.

One particularly negative theory which attempts to account for aggressive behavior is the frustration-aggression hypothesis. The authors of this theory postulated that aggression is always a reaction to some form of frustration in the environment. According to this thinking, the best way to eradicate aggressive behavior in human beings is to implement methods of child rearing that attempt to supply the child with unlimited love and a complete removal of all frustrations.

However, this sort of tampering with the aggressive drive would likely be at the expense of initiative and action. Children don't need frustrations eradicated from their experiences. They need to be taught how to marshal and effectively utilize their aggressive energy in the face of frustration.

Another reason for rejecting the idea that frustration always leads to aggression, or is even a frequent cause of aggression, is that research studies have not been supportive of this idea. Seymour Feshbach, for example, after reviewing all of the studies attempting to link aggressiveness with frustration, concluded that frustration only leads to aggression in those individuals who are already predisposed to act aggressively (in the negative sense of aggressiveness). In fact, the studies indicated that if anything, frustration serves as an energizer of behavior; it tends to enhance motivation.

Adaptive Features. Social psychologist Robert White hypothesized that the drive for competence, or effectiveness, in coping with the environment is a basic motivation in all human beings, a biological need, so to speak. He developed this theory while observing children's play. Play, he noted, serves a purpose; it is not simply a way of escaping or avoiding work. All play has in common the attempt to master the environment.

White believed that this motive—he called it the competence motive—was separate from sexuality or aggressiveness or any of the other drives; he believed that it stood alone. Others, however, disagree. Psychoanalyst Clara Thompson, for example, wrote: "Aggression is not necessarily destructive at all. It springs from an innate tendency to grow and master life which seems to be characteristic of all living matter. Only when this life force is obstructed in its development do ingredients of anger, rage, or hate become connected with it."[11] Thus she sees the drive for competence and mastery of the environment as a positive, adaptive aspect of the aggressive drive.

In early life aggressiveness is almost synonymous with activity. Without aggressive energy, there would be no initiative, no mastery of self or surroundings; there would be only a passive experience of helplessness and torpor. Without the aggressive drive, children would never adaptively separate themselves from their mothers. It's through this innate aggressiveness that we all come to establish ourselves as individuals. In fact, those who fail to develop a strong sense of identity are often those in whom aggressive energy has been very effectively squelched in the early years.

If the aggressive drive plays such an important role in any kind of achievement and mastery, then current attempts to stifle it will no doubt be maladaptive in the long run. As Anthony Storr points out in his book *Human Aggression:* "For this same aggressive impulse which can lead to strife and violence also underlies man's urge to independence and achievement. Just as a child could not possibly grow up into an independent adult if it were not aggressive, so an adult must needs continue to express at least part of his aggressive potential if he is to maintain his own autonomy. . . . In mastering intellectual problems, attacking difficulties, sharpening their wits, or penetrating to the heart of a mystery, men are using, however peaceably, energy which, in the last analysis, is derived from the primitive aggressive drive to gain ascendence over the environment."[12]

So here are the positive features of the aggressive drive: it is an active, outward-thrusting energy without which little, either positive or negative, could be accomplished. Every time a person solves a problem, masters a skill, engages in repartee, or gives an opinion, he is making good use of his aggressive drive. On the other hand, whenever someone murders, oppresses, unjustly condemns, attacks, or criticizes, he is making poor use of his aggressive drive.

Because of the forcefulness of this drive, and the great potential it has to be used either constructively or destructively, it needs constant refinement, close supervision, and proper development. I have found the following suggestions of use in maximizing this drive:

Managing the Aggressive Drive.

1. Use aggressive energy to achieve clearly defined, well-conceived purposes or goals. This is the healthiest use of the aggressive drive. This is aggressiveness as it was meant to be utilized. Freud called it sublimation. You simply designate specific goals that you want for yourself and then use your aggressiveness to reach those goals. As you come to realize some of your goals, you create others. New goals serve as targets for aggressive energy. The nobler and more elevating the goals, the more they are in line with your value system and that of your culture, the less inhibited you will feel in vigorously pursuing those goals. Used in this manner, aggressiveness is constructive; through its positive use, both individuals and society benefit.

By maintaining an aggressive, goal-directed mental set, you also provide yourself with a source of strength during low periods in your life. We all have these moments. Put-downs, frustrations, failures, events that erode self-esteem all tempt us to corral our aggressive energy, possibly even to turn it in on ourselves. Well-defined goals help us during these low periods. Even if we are temporarily forced to cease active attempts at achieving them, we can still spend time laying plans and devising strategies for the time when activity will be reawakened. By focusing upon goals, you get your attention off yourself. The pain diminishes. You feel less at the mercy of circumstances and more at the controls of your life.

2. Develop the capacity for disciplined, aggressive, goal-directed thinking. If there is one area in which aggressiveness can be completely unleashed, it is in the process of thinking. The ability to vigorously, aggressively analyze a problem, lay out alternative solutions, and then determine the most auspicious course of action is an invaluable ability. But it is one of the rarest of capacities. As Sir Joshua Logan wrote: "There is no expedient to which a man will not resort to avoid the real labor of thinking."

It's a sad fact about our nation that people prefer to hear simpleminded, unrealistic anodynes in order to avoid thinking through their own problems. Some years ago Miss Lee R. Steiner wrote a book entitled *Where Do People Take Their Troubles?* It describes in pitiful detail the great number of charlatans, "growth-peddlers," advice merchants, and phonies that people seek out. Rather than forming the habit of aggressively thinking through their own problems, people will consult astrologers, psychics, spiritualists, advice-to-the-lovelorn columnists, and a host of other panderers to human weakness.

This is an unfortunate tendency. By relying so heavily on such simple-minded advice, people not only cut themselves off from painful reality, they also sell themselves short by failing to develop their own mental capacities. Every time you seek the advice of others in order to solve a problem that you could solve on your own, you strengthen the image of a helpless person in your own mind. The mind, like a muscle, strengthens with exercise. And self-confidence is quickly mobilized in the person who develops his own capacities for effective problem-solving.

This does not mean that advice from others should never be sought. In this age of specialization, knowledge in a variety of areas is too hard to come by. Advice from others is necessary in order to aid us in solving problems. But the more often we let other people do our problem-solving for us, the more we miss out on opportunities to develop our own minds. Our aggressive energy lies inert; we fail to develop it properly.

Suppose you found yourself in the following situation: You are swimming in the cove of a deserted tropical island. As you leisurely paddle about, you suddenly notice shark fins heading toward you from the deeper part of the ocean. You quickly turn toward the shore only to find another shark fin coming at you from that direction. How would you spend the few seconds you have before they arrive? I'm sure that most people would spend those few seconds frozen in sheer terror. The most adaptive course of action would be to quickly (very quickly) search your mind for a potential solution to the dilemma and then act upon that solution.

Fortunately most of us are never confronted with problems of that severity. But how many people have you seen throw up their hands in helpless submission to simple problems? Ann Landers' column is replete with this sort of abdication of self-responsibility. "Dear Ann: I loaned a friend $20, and he won't pay me back. What should I do?" "Dear Ann: My daughter brings boys home with her from college on the weekends, and they both sleep in her room. My husband and I disapprove, but we don't know what to do." People who ask for this sort of advice cheat themselves. Their minds lie dormant from want of active effort.

Learning to think aggressively is especially valuable for introverted and hypersensitive persons. These people often have trouble expressing or asserting themselves directly, especially in social situations. Sometimes this causes them to avoid all types of aggression. As a result, their aggressive energy lies dormant, or sometimes even turns inward to punish them. In extreme form it can even lead to suicide.

Of course, Christianity has a very clear message about the evils of rampant aggressiveness. We are not to pursue our own goals aggressively to the exclusion of our neighbor's needs. We are not to retaliate aggressively when we've been wronged. But this doesn't mean that we are to avoid all displays of aggressive energy. For even love, I believe, has an element of aggression in it. Christ's love was relentlessly aggressive, overcoming rudeness, rejection, and abuse from others. Paul was also an aggressive apostle, as were almost all of the early Christians. That's why the message spread so rapidly. So while aggressive energy must be channeled and refined, as must all human drives, let's not forget that it is a God-given drive, without which we would be able to do little in the way of worthy work or thinking. The next point should provide an example of a worthy use of aggressive energy.

3. Master subjects or skills of interest to you. I use the word "master" because it suggests greater aggressiveness than the word "learn." You can set out to learn something by passively reading and listening. This is the way, I'm afraid, that most students learn in school. And this sort of learning is the easiest to accomplish; it is passive and relaxed. But it requires little of the aggressive drive. And if it requires little aggressive energy, then little in the way of mastery and thoroughness will be achieved. Learning of this kind is rapidly lost.

The sort of mastery I'm talking about requires effort and aggression. When using the aggressive drive, you don't simply read a book; you attack it. It is like an enemy fortress to be stormed. You don't just read a chapter and then put the book down. You underline key ideas. You ask blunt, tough questions. You attempt to restate the author's main ideas. You ask yourself how he arrived at his conclusions. And you offer your own alternative conclusions. In short, you become like the person about whom it was said, "When he reads a book, it stays read." This same procedure applies to skill learning and learning of any kind, at least learning that uses the aggressive drive.

To a great extent, this adaptive use of aggressive energy can compensate for disadvantages in intelligence. I have had students (though not very many) who set about to master material in the manner described above. They were usually able to out-learn and out-achieve their brighter but less aggressive classmates. The sad thing is that this type of adaptive aggressiveness is so rare. When it does occur, it is all too often discouraged by those who fear appropriate aggressiveness in others. The highly competent student is often rejected by his peers, at least in grade school. The aggressive young executive bubbling over with initiative and new ideas soon learns to keep his suggestions to himself. This is shameful. We should encourage proper initiative and appreciate it in others, even in those who are able to out-achieve us. If we are afflicted with a bout of envy, then that is the time to aggressively involve ourselves in our own goals. That is the best cure of envy and jealousy.

4. Throw yourself into some sort of exercise program. With all the stresses and pressures of a modern-day urban society, physical exercise would seem almost crucial for mental health. Once aggressiveness is aroused, it does not dissipate easily; unless you physically work off

aggressive energy you will soon experience a state of helplessness and passivity. One study revealed that in a hockey game, the active players were more likely to experience the positive aggressive emotions than the goal keeper, whose chemical state seemed to indicate the presence of passive anxiety. We can rarely act upon every aggressive impulse in a civilized society (in fact, this would be unhealthy in any society), but we drain off our aggressiveness and use it adaptively by throwing ourselves into vigorous physical exercise.

5. Avoid criticism. Excessive criticism promotes passivity. The minute you begin to indulge an overcritical nature, you become a complainer rather than a doer. Critics are like the dogs on my block. Their sole function in life seems to be barking at people (especially joggers) who pass them by. They do nothing themselves, and they are antagonistic (critical?) toward those who do. People who are busy using their aggressive energy constructively rarely have the time or inclination to reroute it into criticism. But people who passively put their fate into the hands of others are often the most critical. The favorite definition of a literary critic is "someone who couldn't make it as a writer."

But criticism is non-adaptive for another reason. It breeds dissatisfaction and discontent. Marital counselors point out that criticism will soon ruin a marriage. And the same thing goes for a business, a company, a school, and a country. When reading the newspaper or watching the news on television sometime, count the number of times a group or individual has something critical to say about the way the government is being run. Then contrast that with the number of times someone makes a well-thought-out, constructive suggestion about a possible solution to a problem. I dare say that the ratio will be heavily weighted toward the former side. This is sad because this country is fast becoming one of the most discontented nations in the world. Creative problem-solving is giving way to passivity and negativism.

6. Teach children to properly channel their aggressive energy; don't squelch their attempts at mastery and initiative. The aggressive drive is a strong drive. The number of wars, hostilities, murders, attacks, etc., occurring all over the world attest to the force of this drive. It is too strong ever to be effectively squelched. In fact, as mentioned before, to do so would be harmful in the long run because it would also stop all positive initiative.

Suppression of the aggressive drive can actually lead to an increase in violent acts of aggression. Sometimes the aggression may be turned inward in the form of suicide. The classical suicidal personality is someone whose flow of aggressive energy has been blocked from the outside world and is therefore turned inward on himself. These individuals frequently come from homes in which outbursts of initiative and aggressiveness on the part of the child are quickly stifled by the parents. Such a person never learns to effectively use his aggressive drive. The results of this suppression can be seen among so-called "shy murderers." For example, in one study a series of personality tests were given to a large group of convicted murderers in order to discover their usual method of handling the aggressive drive. Two types of murderers were discovered: those who were undercontrolled in handling the aggressive drive (as would be expected) and those who were overcontrolled. The former group had a history of fights, violent crimes, assaults, etc., while the latter group up to the time of their crime had been overinhibited, overcontrolled, very well-socialized individuals. In fact, they had been too well socialized. They lacked the ability to be even mildly aggressive. They committed murders when the buildup of aggression became intolerable.

The stifling of aggressive energy also often renders a person ineffective in pursuing his goals. Psychiatrist Frederic Flach talks about the results of having been reared in a family that discourages all aggressiveness: "As a result of an unusually repressive childhood and adolescence, for example, in which initiative and creativity were seldom encouraged and conformity was demanded, a young man may develop serious obstacles to his ability to mobilize his energy and direct his inherent aggression outward toward self-selected goals."[13]

So the way to handle aggressive energy is to use it in the manner God intended: as a source of initiative, competence, and mastery. Aggressive energy shouldn't be allowed completely free reign, and it certainly shouldn't be used to hurt or take advantage of others. But neither should it be squelched. It is too valuable a source of energy.

NOTES

1. Frank Barron, *Creative Person and Creative Process* (New York: Holt, Rinehart, and Winston, 1969).
2. William James, *Pragmatism* (New York: New American Library, 1965).
3. Samuel J. Beck, *Rorschach's Test: A Variety of Personality Pictures*, Vol. 2 (New York: Grune & Stratton, 1967).
4. Zygmunt Piotrowski, *Perceptanalysis, Ex Libris* (1974).
5. Louis Bisch, *Be Glad You're Neurotic!* (New York: McGraw-Hill, 1946).
6. Michael Wallach, "Creativity." In Paul H. Mussen, *Carmichael's Manual of Child Psychology,* 3rd ed. (New York: Wiley, 1970).
7. George W. Crane, *Guidebook for Counseling: How to Cash in on Your Worries* (Mellott, Ind.: Hopkins Syndicate, 1956).
8. Stanley Schacter and Jerome Singer, "Cognitive, Social, and Physiological Determinants of Emotional State," *Psychological Review,* Vol. 69, 1962.
9. J. D. Unwin, *Sex and Culture* (London: Oxford University Press, 1932).
10. Pitirim A. Sorokin, *The American Sex Revolution* (Boston: Porter Sargent, 1956).
11. Clara Thompson, *Interpersonal Psycho-Analysis* (New York: Basic Books, 1964).
12. Anthony Storr, *Human Aggression* (New York: Atheneum, 1968).
13. Frederic Flach, *The Secret Strength of Depression* (Philadelphia: J. B. Lippincott, 1974).

CHAPTER EIGHT
THE ENERGIZING POWER OF LOVE

It would be amiss to write a book on energy without including a chapter on love, the most powerful energizing force. Love is more powerful than 115 volts of electricity. It can motivate and energize human behavior as nothing else can. I remember reading a newspaper account several years back about a woman who came out of a store to find her son pinned beneath the wheels of a car. Several spectators had gathered around, a few strong men among them, but no one knew what to do. This mother, impelled by love, ran up, grabbed that car, and lifted it off of her son. She tore seven muscles in her back, but her love was much more powerful than the demands placed upon her body. Love is like that. It causes us to overlook our own needs and feelings out of concern for the needs and feelings of others.

For this reason, loving people are always energetic. They seem to have the ability to handle any demands placed upon them, to overcome any stresses, and to work continuously, motivated by a spirit of loving service.

The energizing power of love is nowhere better illustrated than in the life of Christ. His work on this earth was characterized by stressful situations, many sleepless nights, and incessant demands, all of which he met with an unflagging source of energy—the energy of love.

One of the best examples of the power of love is presented in Matthew 8. This chapter speaks about a "great multitude" who followed Jesus, eager to gather in the new ideas he espoused. Soon the sick came to be healed, among them a leper and the centurion's servant. Jesus lovingly responded to each demand, his patience never flagging even though they allowed him no rest.

No sooner did Jesus try to seek a few moments' rest at Peter's house than he found Peter's mother-in-law in need of healing. Then "when the even was come, they brought him many that were possessed with devils, and he cast out the spirits with his word, and healed all that were sick." So, at the end of the day Jesus was still working, still meeting incessant demands, as he had been all day without a moment for rest or privacy.

But his work didn't stop there, and neither did his energy. Again Jesus was besieged by the multitude who were pressing about him, some out of curiosity, others out of sincere desire. Jesus got into one of the disciple's boats and instructed them to row to the other side of the lake. From

sheer exhaustion, he collapsed in sleep on the
boat ride over, a sleep so deep that the roaring
thunder and violent waves didn't awaken him.
Right away he was called upon to calm the angry
seas, another demand he met with patience and
love.

When Jesus finally arrived in "the country of
the Gergesenes" yet another stressful demand was
there to greet him. The two men with devils
rushed upon him and his disciples, the latter
fleeing in terror as a result. Still Jesus rose to
the occasion, healed the possessed men, and
patiently took time to instruct them. Later he
received no praise and thanks but rejection and
hostility from the townfolk because of his loving
deed. All this he met with discipline, energy, and
patience.

Only through the energizing power of love
could Christ have successfully met all these
demands. The only people who show this kind of
energy are those who are thoroughly imbued
with the spirit of love. This love doesn't produce
an excitable, impulsive disposition—the personality style we usually associate with energy. Christ
was calm, peaceful, and controlled. His energy
was focused and intense. Little was wasted. But it
was there to meet every demand.

This same focused energy has characterized
all Christ's followers. Each of them was able
to call up enough reserves of energy to meet
the weightiest tasks, the most demanding
responsibilities. This was the style of Moses,
for example, whose love for his own people

enabled him to stand forty years of belligerent complaining in their wilderness exile. This was the style of the disciples after Pentecost, when the Spirit of God (the Spirit of love) filled them to capacity, and impelled them out into the world with one of the most energetic campaigns ever witnessed on the face of the earth.

Love has its roots in the family. Unless the home is a place where love is freely exchanged, and demonstrations of love are encouraged, there will be little loving energy in the character to build upon. Several cultures have been studied in which members live to be over 100 years of age, most notably the Hunzas, Caucasans, and the Vilcahamba. In general, all three cultures live by most of the principles outlined in this book: they exercise, eat sparingly (usually only one or two meals a day) of mainly natural foods, and most importantly they have close-knit, loving family relationships. One 100-year-old Caucasan man said, "If a man has a good and kind wife, he can easily live 100 years."[1]

There's more to love than that, though. For in these three cultures, unlike America, old people are highly respected and warmly regarded. They are considered founts of wisdom and knowledge. They have useful work to perform and important roles to fill in training young people and giving political advice. As a result, people are *optimistic* about the future—about their later years. This optimism results from the love they are given. And the love enables them to live long, energetic lives.

In this country we are rapidly moving toward the time when all old people will be farmed out to nursing homes and all children sentenced to day care centers. Already we have become obsessed with the notion of independence. One study of the child-rearing practices of over thirty cultures revealed that the United States attempts to teach its children to be independent at a far earlier age than any of the other cultures. Perhaps this is one reason why America also leads the rest of the world in neuroses and suicides. We can't imbue our children (and our families) with love when we try to push them out of the nest at the earliest possible chance. And we can't have the sort of loving relationships in marriage that we need when we promote the idea that husband and wife are two independent, self-sufficient personalities. We need to recognize that a part of love is accepting our mutual dependency.

Another aspect of love is forgiveness. Much vital energy is needlessly eaten up in people who can't forgive others who have wronged them. There is an energy-inspiring peace that results from letting go of resentments and grudges. But this peace can usually only be found through prayer and God's Word.

A final aspect of love is the call it gives for service. One of the reasons why love is such an effective energizer is because it must flow outward. It can't be bottled up. It just naturally expresses itself in activity. The person who loves is so wrapped up in serving a cause that's bigger than he that his energy flows outward almost without effort. And this is the most powerful energy of all. It is the sort of energy that makes life worth living.

NOTES

1. Alexander Leaf and John Launois, *Youth in Old Age* (New York: McGraw-Hill, 1975).